EDITORIAL

The 'Hunt' class minehunter HMS *Brocklesby*, 13 June 1983.   *L & L van Ginderen*

Mine warfare is seldom the foremost preoccupation of navies or indeed of those who write about them yet now and then it causes headlines and tensions that reverberate around the world. Such has been the case in Central America with the covert CIA-sponsored mining off Nicaragua's Pacific ports. These operations cause more than just physical damage, and in this instance, apparently 13 ships of several nations were damaged, they can sour relations between states far and wide and cause domestic dissension in the country at whose behest the mining is done. In a way mining evokes the same kind of outrage at sea that chemical warfare arouses on land. Its immediate tactical value may be outweighed by the lingering diplomatic complications and the continuing presence of unswept fields.

The mere threat of mining can influence naval deployments as witness the longstanding belief that Iran can mine the Straits of Hormuz. British minesweepers were sent to the Mediterranean partly because of the US Navy is still woefully deficient in both numbers of minesweepers and their quality. American reliance on helicopters and aircraft both for minelaying and minesweeping has meant that there is no naval organisation specifically devoted to the task; a paradoxical state of affairs when the 1972 mining of Haiphong was the most successful (at least in the short term) operation of its kind since 1945.

Minelaying is militarily cheap and relatively simple compared with missile or torpedo engagements. Almost any craft, airborne, surface or underwater can be quickly adapted to lay mines, and of course they can be laid from the shore. Operation Starvation, the US mining offensive against Japan in 1945, sank or damaged one ship for every 23 mines laid quite apart from its disruptive effects and Japanese resources tied up in mine-counter measures. In the European theatre RAF Bomber Command virtually closed the Baltic in a minelaying campaign also completely overshadowed by the simultaneous strategic bombing campaign.

An excellent illustration of the potency of minelaying comes in Frank Abelsen's account of the Norwegian second class gunboat *Tyr*. An historic leftover even by 1940, she nevertheless laid mines that did damage to the German invasion fleet out of all proportion to her own military value. Substantially more Axis warships and more Royal Navy ships were sunk by mines in 1939-45 than by any other single cause, even air attack.

The mine is the submarine's second weapon and as far as the modern US submarine is concerned, two can be carried for every one torpedo. NATO's future barrier strategy against the Warsaw Pact underwater fleet relies heavily on the US Mark 60 Captor encapsulated torpedo, really a tethered deepwater ASW mine that releases a torpedo on command. This ambitiously advanced piece of technology, product of research going as far back as 1961, has still to be operational but remains a relatively inexpensive item. The Pentagon's 1984 Fiscal Year defence budget proposals aimed to buy 500 for $151.4 million or $302,800 per unit, not a large amount compared with its submarine target.

Stocks of mines remain closely guarded secrets. Estimates of Soviet holdings run up to the half million mark (almost more than were laid by all the combatants in World War II), but a more reliable statistic is that the Warsaw Pact possesses 408 mine-countermeasures vessels to NATO's 235. Another bleak shortfall for a defensive alliance, in an area where numbers can never be too high.

The complexity and cost of minehunting forced France, Belgium and Holland into the 1974 Tripartite minehunter project for 45 vessels, but the number in service is not yet in double figures. At least, however, the current orders by the US Navy (for 14 mine-countermeasures vessels) and the Royal Navy for both glass reinforced plastic minehunters and trawler-minesweepers (the Extra-Deep Armed Team Sweeping concept) are beginning to provide modern ships capable of detecting and neutralising an unpleasant range of sea mines.   **Randal Gray**

We apologise for the non-appearance of the advertised article on 'Hunt' class MCMV and hope to publish it at a later date.

Marconi Class Submarines at War

By Pierre Hervieux

Da Vinci in 1940. She was the top scoring Italian submarine of
World War II.
Author's collection/courtesy of A Fraccaroli

The six boats of this class were built under the 1938
programme, they were a Bernadis design, derived from
the *Marcello* class. Compared with the earlier class the
beam was reduced and length increased as well as
range. More powerful motors provided for a slight
improvement in speed. The diving limit was 330ft and
one less gun was carried to compensate for the lower
stability of the new hull dimensions. These boats are
considered to have been the best Italian ocean-going
submarines built before World War II. During 1941–42
the conning tower was modified in all the boats, size
was reduced and the periscope sleeves were lowered.

Only half the class *(Marconi, Bianchi* and *Da Vinci)*
served in the Mediterranean before being transferred
to the Atlantic. Admiral Sir James Somerville's Force
H attacked the French warships at Mers-el-Kebir on 3
July 1940 and on the day before at 2330 (all times
given are German) *Marconi* (Capt Chialamberto)
launched torpedoes and missed the destroyer HMS

Baracca in Italian waters before being moved to the Atlantic
1940.

Author's collection/courtesy of A Fraccaroli

Voritgern (1917, 1090 tons) off Gibraltar. Force H was
again attacked by *Marconi* on 11 July east of Gibraltar
and this time the destroyer HMS *Escort* (1934, 1405
tons) was torpedoed and sunk 36° 20′N/03° 46′W during Operation MA 5. On 25 July 1940 the Italian proposal for establishing a base for Italian submarines in
occupied France to operate in the Atlantic was
accepted by the Germans. As a result on 1 September
1940 the new Italian base, named BETASOM, opened
at Bordeaux under the command of Rear Admiral A
Parona. *Malaspina* (Capt Leoni) forced the Gibraltar
Strait on 3 August 1940 operated in the area of the
Azores and then proceeded to Bordeaux. On her way
she torpedoed and sank the British tanker *British Fame*
(1936, 8046 tons, 0550, 37° 44′N/22° 56′W) on 12
August. This tanker belonged to the dispersed convoy
OB 193. On 19 August an 8000-ton unidentified cargo
ship was missed with one torpedo (0120, 39° 20′N/21°
25′W). From 17 August *Bianchi* (Capt Giovannini)

operated off Gibraltar claiming to have torpedoed and
sunk an anti-submarine trawler on 25 August (0603);
in fact she missed her.

From 27 August a second wave of Italian submarines
was moved in two groups from the Mediterranean to
Bordeaux, among them were *Baracca* (Capt Bertarelli)
and *Torelli* who operated in the area between Portugal,
the Azores and Madeira. The *Marconi* operating off
NW Spain. On 4 September *Maslaspina* reached Bordeaux, being the first of 32 Italian submarines to be
based in the French harbour for the next three years.
On 19 September 1940 *Marconi* torpedoed and sank
the Spanish trawler *Almirante Jose de Carranza* (1918,
330 tons, 0315, 43′N/09′W).

On 23 September *Da Vinci* (Capt Calda) was transferred to the Atlantic and like her sister boats passed
safely through the Gibraltar Strait and operated in the
area of the Azores and Madeira. On 28 September
1940 *Marconi* arrived at Bordeaux. On 1 October
Baracca sank with gunfire the Greek cargo ship *Aghios
Nicolaos* (1915, 3687 tons , 0415, 40′N/16° 55′W) and
arrived at Bordeaux on 6 October, the *Torelli* having
arrived on the 5th. On 9 October the *Malaspina* was the
first to proceed to the North Atlantic from Bordeaux.
In the course of October *Baracca* and *Marconi* followed. On 20 October *Malaspina* claimed to have torpedoed and sunk (?) an 8000-ton unidentified cargo
ship from the dispersed convoy OB 229, 59°N/29°W.
Da Vinci reached Bordeaux on 31 October. On her way
to Bordeaux, *Bianchi*, last boat of the class, got into
difficulties. On 4 November she had to put in to Tangier after being bombed by a London flying boat of No
202 Squadron RAF and depth charged by the destroyer
HMS *Greyhound* and damaged. On 8 November *Marconi* in attempting to maintain contact with the convoy
HX 84 was depth charged by the destroyer HMS
Havelock but was able next day to put a finishing torpedo into the Swedish cargo ship *Vingaland* (1935,
2734 tons, 55° 41′N/18° 24′) which had been set on fire
by a German FW 200 Condor plane. *Baracca* torpedoed and sank the British cargo ship *Lilian Moller*

TABLE 1: MARCONI CLASS OUTLINE

	Builders	Laid down	Launched	Completed
Guglielmo Marconi	CRDA, M	19.9.38	30.7.39	20.2.40
Leonardo Da Vinci	CRDA, M	19.9.38	16.9.39	7.4.40
Michele Bianchi	OTO, M	15.2.39	3.12.39	15.4.40
Luigi Torelli	OTO, M	15.2.39	6.1.40	15.5.40
Alessandro Malaspina	OTO, M	1.3.39	18.2.40	20.6.40
Maggiore Baracca	OTO, M	1.3.39	21.4.40	10.7.40

CRDA,M = Cantieri Riuniti Dell'Adriatico, Monfalcone.
OTO,M = Odero, Terni, Orlando, Muggiano (La Spezia).

Displacement	1191 tons surfaced/1498 tons submerged.
Displacement	251ft (76.50m) OA × 22ft 4in (6.81m) × 15ft 6in (4.72m)
Machinery	2 sets CRDA diesels, 3600hp/2 sets Marelli electric motors 1500hp.
Oil	118 tons
Maximum speed	17.8 knots surfaced/8.2 knots submerged
Range	2900 miles at 17 knots surfaced, 10,500 miles at 8 knots surfaced, 110 miles at 3 knots submerged, 80 miles at 4 knots submerged, 8 miles at 8 knots submerged.
Armament	3.9in (100mm) 47-cal gun, four 13.2mm AA machine guns (2×2). Eight 21in (533mm) torpedo tubes (4 forward, 4 aft) with 12 torpedoes.
Complement	7 officers plus 50 petty officers and seamen

Malaspina arriving in Bordeaux on 4 September 1940.
Author's collection/E C P Armées

(1913, 4866 tons) belonging to the dispersed convoy SLS 53 on 18 November (1740, 57°N/17°W). On 13 December *Bianchi* left Tangier for Bordeaux where she arrived on the 18th.

OPERATIONS IN 1941

Da Vinci operated in the North Atlantic for the first 18 days of January west of North Channel, without success. *Malaspina* and *Torelli* were deployed against convoys. The former had no success, but *Torelli* torpedoed and sank the Greek cargo ship *Nemea* on 15 January (1919, 5101 tons, 2120 52° 33'N/24° 13'); 28 minutes later she torpedoed and sank the Norwegian cargo ship *Brask* (1911, 4079 tons 52° 45'N/23° 59'W). The following day at 0100 *Torelli* sank with torpedo and gunfire the Greek cargo ship *Nicolaos Flinis* (1904, 3111 tons) 53°N/24°W. On 28 January 2100 she torpedoed and sank a fourth ship, the British SS *Urla* (1924, 5198 tons, 2100, 54° 54'N/19'W). Between 16 January and 22 February *Marconi* operated unsuccessfully off Portugal. By the end of January *Baracca* operated west of the North Channel and Ireland without scoring. In mid-February she was relieved by *Bianchi* which on the 14th torpedoed and sank the British SS *Belrest* (1925,

4517 tons, 21° 54'/21'W), a straggler from convoy SC 21. On the 19th *Bianchi* was ordered to operate against convoy OB 287 but failed to reach it that day because of an inaccurate FW 200 Condor sighting report. She encountered a stubborn adversary on the 23rd (2242) the British Ocean Boarding vessel HMS *Manistee* (1920, 5368 tons) which had already been damaged by a torpedo from *U 107*, but the crew succeeded in getting the ship under way again at 8 knots within 30 minutes of the hit. At 1056, *Bianchi* also fired but missed as did *U 107* with three duds! It was not until the morning of the 24th after further attempted attacks by both Axis boats that *U 107* (Capt Hessler) finally sank *Manistee* with a double fan salvo at 59° 30'N/21'. On the same say *Bianchi* was more skilful and luckier when at 0345 she torpedoed and sank the British SS *Linaria* (1924, 3385 tons, 61°N/25°W) from the dispersed convoy OB 288 which had been found by another Condor on the 22nd.

Following *U 47*'s contact report *Bianchi* was ordered to attack convoy OB 290 but did not come up. On the 27th (0145) she attacked and slightly damaged with gunfire the British SS *Empire Ability* (ex-German *Uhenfels*, 1931, 7603 tons) from convoy OB 290. Shortly later, at 0447, *Bianchi* torpedoed and sank the British SS *Baltistan* (1937, 6803 tons at 51° 52'/19° 55'), a straggler from the same convoy. On 18 April *Da*

Marconi arriving in Bordeaux on 28 September 1940.
Author's collection/E C P Armées

Vinci, Torelli and *Malaspina* began patrolling west of Ireland. On the 22nd *Torelli* sighted a homewardbound convoy but was unable to call in U-boats. The same happened with an outwardbound convoy next day. Between 9 and 30 April *Baracca* operated unsuccessfully west of Gibraltar. On 3 May (2120) at 55°N/21°W

Marconi in Bordeaux with a modified conning tower, July 1941.
Author's collection/E C P Armées

Malaspina (Capt Prini) launched torpedoes and missed the British passenger liner *Lycaon* (1913, 7350 tons). Six days later *Torelli* was deployed without success against a Condor-sighted convoy west of Iceland. *Bianchi* and *Malaspina* were likewise against another convoy.

An Italian submarine group of 7 boats operated against convoys W of Gibraltar between 25 May and 16 June. Among them was *Marconi* (Capt Pollina) which on 30 May torpedoed and sank the Royal Navy tanker *Cairndale* (1938, 8129 tons) 35°N/09°W). Then on 1 June (1452) *Marconi* sank with her 3.9in gun the unmarked Portuguese trawler *Exportador* (1917, 318 tons, 36°N/09°W). Then on the 6th she attacked convoy OG 63 between 0422 and 0427 launching torpedoes at a tanker and three cargo ships. Two of the latter were hit and sunk, they were the British *Baron Lovat* (1926, 3395 tons, 0425, 33° 30′N/11° 30′W) and the Swedish *Taberg* (1920, 1392 tons, 0427, 35° 36′/11° 12′W).

Between 24 June and 17 July an Italian submarine group operated against convoys West of Gibraltar. On 28 June (1254) *Da Vinci* (Capt Calda) torpedoed and sank the British tanker *Auris* (1935, 8030 tons, 34° 27′/11° 57′W) sailing independently. *Bianchi* left Bordeaux on 4 July to join this group but was torpedoed and sunk by the British submarine *Tigris* (Capt Bone) the next day at 45° 03′N/04° 01′W. Repeated radio calls between 12 and 18 July drew no reply. Also on the 5th

Torelli (Capt De Giacomo) sighted one small convoy proceeding westward to which *Da Vinci*, *Baracca* and *Malaspina*. Only *Torelli* was able to make an unsuccessful attack on a destroyer. On 7 July *Torelli* sighted another outwardbound convoy to which *Da Vinci* and *Baracca* were directed, but they did not find what was probably HG 66. But a week later at 2215 *Malaspina* torpedoed and sank the Greek Cargo ship *Nikoklis* (1921, 3576 tons, 36°N/21°W) from the dispersed convoy OG 67. On 17 July she torpedoed and sank the British cargo ship *Guelma* (1928, 44402 tons, 1695, 30° 44′/17° 33′W). Next day it was reported that agents had seen convoy HG 67 from Gibraltar. *Malaspina* and

Torelli arriving in St Nazaire on 23 December 1941 with part of the crew of the German auxiliary cruiser *Atlantis*. Note the modified conning tower.
Author's collection/E C P Armées

Torelli in Bordeaux on 5 October 1940.
Author's collection/E C P Armées

TABLE 2: SHIPS SUNK BY THE 6 MARCONI CLASS SUBMARINES

Da Vinci	17 merchant ships = 120,243 tons (the Italian top score of World War II)		
Torelli	7 merchant ships = 42,871 tons		
Marconi	1 destroyer, 1 RN Fleet Oiler =	9534 tons	20,292 tons
	6 merchant ships	10,758 tons	
Malaspina	3 merchant ships = 16,384 tons		
Bianchi	3 merchant ships = 14,705 tons		
Baracca	3 merchant ships = 8987 tons		
TOTAL	39 merchant ships		
	1 destroyer	= 223,482 tons	
	1 RN Fleet Oiler		

Torelli, together with 3 other Italian boats, were concentrated against them but the convoy evaded them.

On the 21st *Torelli* succeeded in torpedoing and sinking the Norwegian tanker *Ida Knudsen* (1925, 8913 tons, 2134, 34° 34′N/13° 14′W). On 9 August convoy HG 69's departure from Gibraltar was also reported, *Marconi* and two other boats were directed against it along with several U-boats. On 11 August (0335, 37°N/10°W) *Marconi* fired at but missed the British sloop *Deptford* (1935, 990 tons) and the corvette *Convolvulus* (1940, 925 tons), part of HG 69's escort. *Marconi* continued to send shadowing reports despite interruptions until she was driven off on 14 August. That same day at 0001 *Marconi* destroyed with gunfire the independent cargo ship *Sud* (1901, 2589 tons, 41°N/18°W) with 25 rounds of 3.9in. *U 126* (Capt Bauer) finished off the wreck with a torpedo. The operation was broken off the next day (15 August). *Marconi* was redirected during 20–24 August to hunt vainly for convoy HG 70 (reported to have left Gibraltar on the 18th). *Baracca*, *Da Vinci* and the other Italian boats had a similar fruitless search for convoy HG 71 (4–6 September). On 8 September *Baracca* (Capt Viani), in taking up a new patrol line, was compelled to surface west of Gibraltar by depth charges from the British escort destroyer *Groome* and, after a short gun engagement, she was sunk by ramming at 0930 in position 40° 15′/20° 55′W. *Baracca* was probably responsible for sinking with her gunfire the small Panamanian cargo ship *Trinidad* (1939, 434 tons, 46° 06′N/17° 04′W) on 5 September. Convoy HG 72 set out from Gibraltar on the 10th being attacked by *Da Vinci* and *Torelli*, but they were driven off by the escort. On the 18th they were redirected towards convoy HG 73, *Torelli* established a brief contact the next day and again during the evening of the 20th only to receive depth charge damage from the destroyer HMS *Vimy* during the night of the 21st-22nd. On the 23rd *Da Vinci* kept contact for a while. Nothing was heard from *Malaspina* after her departure from Bordeaux on 7 September. It is now known that the submarine attacked by *Vimy* was not *Malaspina*; this attack took place at 2115 on 21 September (37° 46′N/19° 18′W) and in addition according to the *Commando Sommergibili*'s orders, *Malaspina*'s position that day would have been about 180 miles farther to the east. *Marconi* left Bordeaux in 5 October and later received orders to attack convoy HG 74 (sighted after midnight on 23 October by *U 71*. *Marconi* was last heard from at 1130 on the 29th when she gave her position as 42° 55′/21° 55′W. She probably sank, by unknown cause, about 300 miles west of Gibraltar. It has been stated that *Marconi* was sunk on 28 November by *U 67*. This is certainly wrong for according to German sources *U 67* was not at sea between the end of September and mid-December. *Marconi* failed to answer radio calls made until 5 November.

On 14 December *Torelli* was in the South Atlantic rescuing part of the crew from the German auxiliary cruiser *Atlantis* (sunk by the cruiser HMS *Devonshire* on 22 November) and brought them into St Nazaire.

OPERATIONS IN 1942

Between 20 February and 24 March 1942 the *Da Vinci* group (5 boats) operated east of the Antilles (Caribbean). At 0027 on 20 February the British cargo ship *Scottish Star* (1917, 7224 tons, 13° 24′N/49° 36′W), was torpedoed and sunk by the *Torelli*. On 25 February *Da Vinci* (Capt Longanesi-Cattani) torpedoed and sank the Brazilian cargo ship *Cabedelo* (1932, 3557 tons, 16°N/49°W). Next day *Torelli* sank with torpedo and gunfire the Panamanian tanker *Esso Copenhagen* (1939, 9245 tons, 10° 32′N/53° 20′W). On 28 February *Da Vinci* sank with torpedo and gunfire the Latvian cargo ship *Everasma* (1920, 3644 tons 17°N/48°W). On 11 March at 0056am *Torelli* launched and missed the

The 100m (3.9in) deck gun forward of a *Marconi* class submarine's conning tower in Bordeaux. These boats made heavy use of their gun armament, in conjunction with torpedoes.
Author's collection/E C P Armées

British SS *Orari* (1931, 10,350 tons, 13°N/57°W); this *Plymouth merchant ship was damaged on two other occasions and also survived.*

After returning to Bordeaux *Torelli* sailed again on 2 June to attack shipping off the Bahamas. Two days out into the Bay of Biscay (0227, 4 June) while running on the surface she was attacked by a plane using a searchlight and flying very low. Surprise was complete when it machine-gunned the boat and dropped bombs that exploded underneath. The heavily damaged boat made for the Spanish coast. The Spanish authorities obligingly towed her to Aviles for five days of repairs. She returned to Bordeaux on 14 July. This was the first time an Italian submarine had been attacked by night by a radar-fitted aircraft in the Bay of Biscay. In June *Da Vinci* sank four ships off West Africa. On the 2nd she sank with torpedo and gunfire the Panamanian sailing vessel *Reine Marie Stewart* (1919, 1087 tons, 07° 16'N/13° 20'W, 2250). On the 7th she torpedoed and sank the British SS *Chile* (1915, 6956 tons, 04° 17'N/13° 48'W). On the 10th it was the turn of the Dutch cargo vessel *Alioth* (1937, 5483 tons, 00° 08'/18° 52'W). On the 13th torpedo and gunfire dispatched the British SS *Clan Macquarrie* (1913, 6471 tons, 05° 30'/23° 30'W). On her return to Bordeaux *Da Vinci* was temporarily modified to carry a CA type midget submarine. This entailed removal of the deck gun and the installation forward of the conning tower of a cell fitted with clamps (shackels) to carry the CA. These could be freed while submerged and could be retrieved by the carrier submarine (known as Kangaroo) while awash. Tests showed that the midgets needed improving before they could be considered operational. The midget was destined to attack ships in New York and Freetown, the attack on New York being scheduled for December 1943 but never took place because Italy's surrender came first. *Da Vinci* left Bordeaux on 7 October and operated without success for the last five days west of the Cape Verde Islands under the command of Captain Gazzana. She switched to the NE coast of Brazil until 14 November with far greater success. On the 2nd *Da Vinci* sank with torpedo and gunfire the British SS *Empire Zeal* (1914, 7000 tons, 00° 30'S/30° 54'W. Next day at 0105 the Italian submarine was forced to crash dive by gunfire from the Dutch ship *Frans Hals* (1941, 6626 tons, 01°S/32°W) after a torpedo had missed. On 4 November *Da Vinci* sent the Greek ship *Andreas* (1919, 6566 tons, 2208, 02° 00'S/30° 30'W) to the bottom with torpedo and gunfire. The same combination accounted for the brand new Liberty ship *Marcus Whitman* (1942, 7176 tons, 0012, 05° 40'S/32° 41'W) at 0012 on the 10th and for the Dutchman *Veerhaven* (1930, 5291 tons, 03° 51'S/32° 41'W) at 0012 on the 10th and for the Dutchman *Veerhaven* (1930, 5291 tons, 03° 51'S/29° 22'W) at 0611 on the 11th.

OPERATIONS IN 1943

Torelli left Bordeaux in February 1943 and operated off the Brazilian coast without luck. She was attacked by aircraft off Fernando de Noronha on 16 March,

shooting one down with her 13.2mm AA guns, but she was left damaged, unable to submerge and leaking fuel. She returned to base. *Da Vinci* sailed, for the last time from Bordeaux on 20 February to operate in the Indian Ocean. Outwardbound in the South Atlantic she torpedoed and sank, on 14 March the British liner *Empress of Canada* (1922, 21,517 tons, 01° 13'S/09° 57'W). Then on the 19th at precisely midnight she torpedoed and sank the British SS *Lulworth Hill* (1940, 762 tons, 10° 10'S/01° 00'E). Reaching the Indian Ocean on 17 April she torpedoed and sank the Dutch cargo ship *Sembilan* (1922, 6566 tons, 31° 30'S/33° 30'E). Next day torpedo and gunfire sank the British SS *Manaar* (1942, 8007 tons, 30° 59'S/33° 00'E.) On the 21st the same means sank the US Liberty ship *John Drayton* (1942, 7177 tons, 32° 10'S/34° 50'E) and lastly the British tanker *Doryssa* (1938, 8078 tons 37° 03'S/24° 03'E). On her return voyage *Da Vinci* signalled Bordeaux on 22 May that she would arrive in a week's time. But next day at 1145 (GMT) the frigate HMS *Ness*, escorting a convoy, obtained a submarine contact with her asdic. She and the destroyer HMS *Active* dropped depth charges until the contact was lost. The submarine was *Da Vinci* and she was destroyed about 300 miles west of Vigo in Spain.

This left *Torelli* as the sole survivor of the class and she was extensively modified to carry cargo to the Far East by the end of May 1943. On 18 June she sailed from Bordeaux on the long voyage to the Indian Ocean with 130 tons of mercury, special steel in bars, 20mm gun mountings, a new pattern of 500kg aircraft bomb. Near St Helena *Torelli* escaped undamaged from an aircraft attack but was obliged to lengthen her course with the unpleasant result that she ran out of fuel in the Indian Ocean. After an unsuccessful rendezvous with a refuelling U-boat, BETASOM was able to organise a second successful one. A replenished *Torelli* kept on, was met by the Italian colonial sloop *Eritrea* and reached Sabang (Sumatra) on 26 August 1943. When Italy surrendered, *Torelli* was about to leave Singapore for Bordeaux with a valuable cargo. She was seized by the Japanese on 10 September. She was then handed over to the Germans who renamed her *UIT 25* and kept the boat until 10 May 1945 when she was handed back to Japan and enrolled into the Imperial Navy on 15 July unarmed as *I-504*. Found at Kobe on 2 September, she was scuttled off this harbour by the US Navy on 1 April 1946. *Torelli* had been a lucky vessel like the cargo ship *Orari* she missed! Compared to her sisters *Malaspina* and *Marconi* who disappeared without known cause, she survived serious damage three times, once from the destroyer HMS *Vimy* (21 September 1941) and twice from aircraft attacks (4 June and 16 March).

GRAF ZEPPELIN Part I

By M J Whitley

Despite the relatively advanced state of aircraft development in Germany during the First World War, little progress was made in the field of shipboard aviation, mainly due to the existence of the Zeppelin fleet, of which great things were expected. However, the only naval use made of the Zeppelins was for reconnaisance on a limited scale and they were more frequently employed on air raids over the British Isles. The wide-scale use of aircraft from flying-off platforms mounted on the turrets of Grand Fleet battleships was never initiated by the High Seas Fleet and even the seaplane carrier, of which the Royal Naval put nine into service, appeared to have held little interest for the German naval staff. Only one ship, the light cruiser *Stuttgart*, was actually converted for this purpose late in the war, being equipped with two hangars aft and able to operate three floatplanes. As the conversion was not completed until May 1918, her operational service was almost non-existent and after the surrender she was allocated to Britain and scrapped.

A further project to convert the obsolete cruiser *Roon* into an aircraft mother ship never left the drawing board. Apart from *Stuttgart*, only the raider *Wolf* made operational use of a scout floatplane but another brief use of shipboard aircraft does deserve mention even though it was only of a temporary nature. In the summer of 1916, an air attack on the port installations of Reval in the Gulf of Finland could only be carried out by using torpedo boats to ferry the low endurance floatplanes to a starting point offshore within their flying range. Four aircraft were so transported, one per torpedo boat, shipped on the after torpedo tubes. This was just one special operation and cannot truly be categorised as 'naval aviation'.

Only one attempt at producing a true aircraft carrier was seriously made. This was to have been the conversion of the Italian liner *Ausonia* which had been lying incomplete at the Blohm & Voss yard since her launching in April 1915. Her reconstruction would have followed the lines of that carried out to produce the British *Argus* except that the German ship would have had a proper bridge, funnel and superstructure on the starboard side. This was an advance on the *Argus* design whose retractable wheelhouse and horizontal smoke ducts in lieu of funnels led to problems in operational use. In another respect, however, the German design was behind the times for separate landing and flying off decks were envisaged, despite the availability of a flush deck from stem to stern. A mixture of floatplanes and wheeled fighters, totalling about 30 aircraft were to be accommodated. The ship was coal fired, with twin-shaft 18,000hp geared turbine machinery giving a speed of 21 knots. Curiously, both British and German conversions were from Italian liners. The German project came too late, however, for by late 1918, the war had been lost and it is doubtful if any work was actually carried out on the ship.

The collapse and surrender of Germany in November 1918 put an end to any further experiments and the Versailles Treaty of 1919 effectively killed any hope of future German naval aviation by prohibiting aircraft, their development and aircraft cariers. This situation pertained until the late 1920s and 1930s, when in a changed political climate, clandestine experiments with aircraft began again.

These undercover activities were mainly directed at the future information of a land-based air force but the *Reichsmarine* did, in October 1928, lay the foundations of a naval air arm, when it obtained government approval for a few seaplanes for 'experimental' purposes. The excuse for this was the fact that the Versailles Treaty allowed the *Reichsmarine* to retain anti-aircraft guns. This was interpreted as also permitting aircraft to tow the necessary targets for training purposes! In this way, an organisation known as 'Air Service Incorporated' was formed as a cloak for its illegitimate activities with the Fleet. Although eventually killed off with the advent of Hermann Goering and his 'Everything which flies belongs to me' attitude, this service did constitute the basis of a naval air arm.

In January 1935 the *Reichsminister der Luftfahrt*, Erhard Milch had laid down the agreed strength, composition and dispositions of the Naval Air Arm. Included amongst these was the provision for three carrier-borne *Grüppen*, one for Reconnaissance (*Träger Aufklarungsgrüppe (M) 216*), one General Purpose (*Trägermehrzweckgruppe 286*) and one Dive bomber (*Trägersturzkampfgrüppe 266*). Each *grüppe* comprised a staff fight and three *staffeln*, identified in the usual manner, (ie *1/216,2/216,3/216* etc). Two *gruppen* were to be based at Barge and the dive bombers at Jever when disembarked. All were expected to form on 1 October 1938. Note that at this period, naval aircraft duties were primarily considered to be spotter/reconnaissance and torpedo bomber, no pure fighter role being included. However, from 1935 onwards the small band of trained naval airmen were continually commandeered by the expanding *Luftwaffe*, with the result that the *Reichsmarine* ended up with a truncated force capable of only a few duties. Moreoever, despite this agreement with the *Luftwaffe* that the naval air arm would comprise nine

Tugs manoeuvring *Graf Zeppelin* after her launch at Kiel in Hitler's presence on 10 December 1938.

squadrons of long-range flying boats, 18 multi-purpose squadrons, 12 carrier-borne and two shipboard catapult squadrons, such was the inter-service bickering that only a fraction of this force was available at the outbreak of war.

Thus international politics, treaty restrictions and inter-service rivalry combined with the Navy's seemingly low enthusiasm to delay the building of Germany's first aircraft carrier even though, by the 1930s the type was assuming greater importance in naval tactics, despite formidable opposition from the 'Big Gun' protagonists. Nevertheless the Naval Staff were alive to the possibilities of the type and were considering the construction of carriers at least as early as 1934. On 12 March 1934, the staff requirements for a proposed aircraft carrier were tabled. These were as follows:

MAIN REQUIREMENTS
(a) Theatre of operations, Atlantic & North Seas.
(b) Minimum flight deck length 180m (590ft 7in)
(c) Catapult for single aircraft on forecastle.
(d) Facilities for handling seaplanes.
The ship was to be patterned on *Akagi/Furious/Ranger*.

Displacement	About 15,000 tonnes
Speed	33kts (continuous)
Armament	9 × 150mm or 6 × 203mm guns
Range	12,000 miles

Armour	Cruiser scale
Aircraft	60 (⅓ with folding wings)
Catapults	2

Admiral Raeder's main criticism of this concerned the gun armament. He attached special importance to the astern firepower, being particularly worried about a running chase, for which he considered two triple 230mm (8in) mountings the minimum desirable. This would have caused severe constructional problems as no doubt he realised, for he was prepared to accept one triple 203mm with three more single guns each side in casemates. However, design calculations soon showed the 203mm armament to be impracticable and in any case, only the USA had this calibre in aircraft carriers. Whether it was realised at this time that carriers should rely on their own aircraft and other ships' guns for surface defence is not clear but the calibre had to be reduced to 150mm.

By April 1934, during a conference on future construction it was proposed that an aircraft carrier be included in the 1935 programme. The Treaty of Versailles remained a problem and in view of this, together with the fact that this was a completely new type of vessel (for Germany), the head of the *Marinekommandoamt* proposed that preparations be started, to allow an order to be placed by October 1935.

The formidable task of designing the new ship was entrusted to *Marineoberbaurat* Wilhelm Hadeler, formerly assistant to the Professor of Warship Construction at Berlin University. Hadeler gathered together a design team and made a start on the project, having obtained technical details of the USS *Lexington* and using the Royal Navy's *Courageous* design as a useful starting point. By June 1934 a sketch design had been prepared, which immediately attracted comments and demands for modifications from many sections of the Navy, who appeared to be unsure of their precise requirements of an aircraft carrier. This bickering and indecisiveness was to be a feature of the design process of many a German naval vessel, with consequent long delays before construction commenced. The 'M' type cruisers were a notable example of this and in the case of the carrier, this tortuous process was further complicated by the need to involve a second service, the *Luftwaffe*, whose C-in-C had no love at all for the *Kriegsmarine*.

In June 1935 the Anglo-German Naval Treaty was signed in an effort on the part of Great Britain to impose some form of control on Germany's rearmament, bearing in mind the Versailles restrictions' ineffectiveness. This agreement restricted the German Fleet to 35 per cent of the British but, strangely, did not mention the forbidden category of aircraft carrier by which the Germans inferred a right to legally build 38,500 tons of this category! The *Kriegsmarine* then decided to build two vessels to utilise this tonnage thus forcing Hadeler to re-cast his design, having by this time, arrived at a legend displacement of some 24,000 tonnes following changes in the staff requirements. The major operators of aircraft carriers were the USA, England and Japan and Hadeler was fortunate that relations between his country and Japan were improving steadily (the Anti-Comintern Pact was signed in November 1936) and in conseuence he was able to send a team to Japan to inspect the Imperial Navy's *Akagi*. As a result of this visit, numerous alterations were made to the German design, including the provision of a third life and an extension of the flight deck. Later still, following the successful development of a catapult system by Deutschewerk, it was agreed during a conference on 10 April 1937, to install two such equipments at the forward end of the flight deck.

The design work continued and led to the unveiling of a 12,250 ton (standard) displacement vessel which was actually of 33,550 tonne full load displacement with a speed of 33.8 knots on 200,000hp obtained from a four shaft geared turbine installation utilising the new high pressure steam concept. An aircraft complement of about 40 machines was envisaged with a gun armament consisting of 16 150mm guns (capable of low angle use only) and 10, later 12, 150mm guns was originally to number only eight, in single mountings but a proposal to save weight by utilising twin mountings was misinterpreted and led to eight twin casemates in lieu of the intended four twins. This complicated ammunition supply arrangements and required larger gun crews.

DESIGN FEATURES

The basic design featured a hangar structure and flight deck built on the hull after contemporary US and Japanese practice, in contrast with the more recent British 'all one' concept. Her 250m (820ft 3in) long hull was divided into 21 watertight compartments and incorporated two hangars, one above the above. Three electrically powered 5.5 tonne lifts, each on the centre line, served both hangars. The upper hangar was 185m (606ft 11in) long and the lower one 172m (564ft 4in). Both were 16m (52ft 6in) in width but the lower one had slightly less head room. The flight deck itself, 242m (793ft 11in) in length, was constructed of steel with an anti-splinter protection function and overlaid with a wooden surface. This deck was the upper deck strength deck of the ship. At the forward end of the flight deck, two compressed air catapults capable of launching 5 tonne aircraft at 133km/hr (82.6mph) were installed but the catapult originally envisaged on the forecastle on the British *Courageous* pattern was finally deleted from the design. Each catapult could launch nine aircraft on its own reservoir of air, at a rate of one every half minute. Following this, 50 minutes were required to recharge the reservoirs.

Four arrester wires were provided aft and two emergency wires fore and aft of the centre life. Drawings of the ship in its original form also show four further arrester wires disposed fore and aft of the forward lift, possibly intended to allow recovery of aircraft when the ship was going astern as, it is believed, certain US carriers were originally equipped to do so. On the starboard side was positioned the island superstructure following common practice (except for a few Japanese ships). This was a long, low structure fitting the command and navigating bridges, charthouse etc.

Fore and aft of the island, the secondary armament of 105mm SKC/33 guns in twin mountings was disposed two forward (later three) and three aft. The four 4m flak directors in their distinctive spherical stabilised towers flanked the massive flat topped funnel that dominated the superstructure. A single 7m rangefinder on the bridge was fitted for main (low angle) armament that consisted of 16 150mm SKC/28 guns paired in casements. This provided one of the most distinctive features of the design and had probably been adopted following the pattern of the Japanese *Kaga* and *Akagi* but which, apart from the antiquated French *Béarn*, had not been used by any other nation building aircraft carriers. In fact it had by then also been abandoned by the Japanese themselves.

Internally, there were four main deck levels which were full beam, denoted from keel upwards, hold, lower platform, upper platform and tween deck, of which the latter was the main armoured deck. Above the tween deck, the lower and upper hangars effectively split all other decks up to flight deck level into gallery decks, except at the extremities, where mess decks or work shops closed off the ends of the hangars. These gallery decks were known as decks 'D', 'C', 'B' and 'A' moving upwards to the flight deck, with 'B' deck running the full length of the ship to form forecastle and quarterdeck for working the ship. Much of the ship's company and all *Luftwaffe* personnel were quartered on these decks around the hangar spaces. Officers' accommodation in the form of single and double cabins was on 'A' deck with the officers' mess right forward under the leading edge of the flight deck. The mess could be divided into

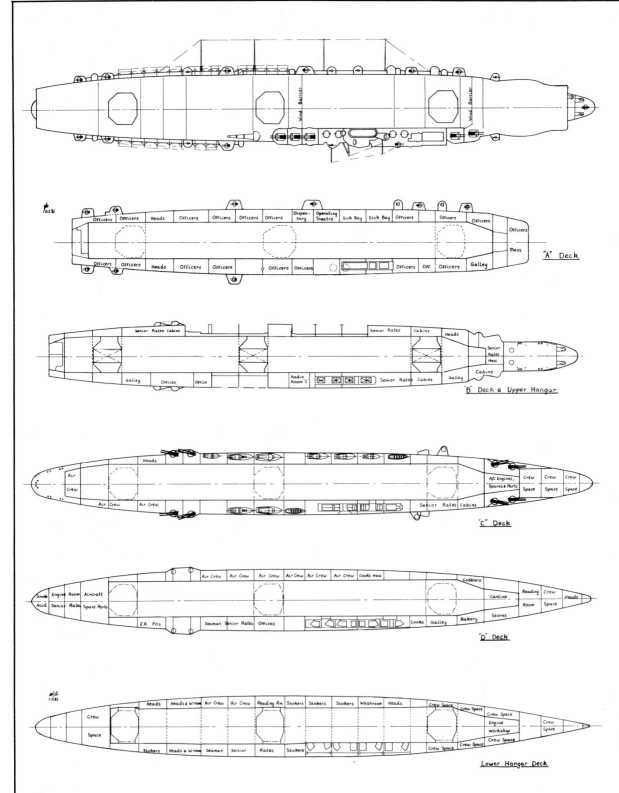

"A" Deck

"B" Deck & Upper Hangar

"C" Deck

"D" Deck

Lower Hangar Deck

Deck plans for the *Graf Zeppelin*.
Author's drawing

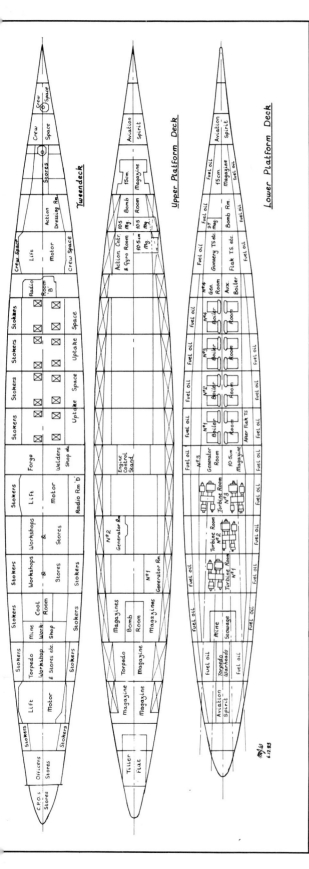

two parts – one Navy, one *Luftwaffe!* Also on 'A' deck to
port was the sick bay, comprehensively equipped with an
X-ray room, operating theatre, isolation room, two
wards, dispensary and ancilliary facilities. The ship's
complement numbered 108 officers (51 air force), and
1612 other ranks (266 air force).

Below the tween deck or armoured deck, the largest
spaces were occupied by the main propulsion machinery
and magazines. Four boiler rooms and three turbine
rooms, together with four generator rooms and an auxiliary boiler room comprised the machinery unit, which
extended from frame stations 66½ to 176 ie 44 per cent of
the ship's length. On the platform decks forward and aft,
the combined magazine and shell rooms for the 150mm
guns served their respective guns via electrical bucket
hoist systems whose supply route was of necessity complicated by the need to serve guns on the beam and thus
be deflected around the hangar spaces. Also at the fore-
ends was a separate magazine for bombs from which a
lift conveyed the ordnance to the lower hangar deck. Aft
was a large magazine for torpedoes with its associated
warhead room below it, a magazine for mines and
another for bombs. Lifts again conveyed the mines and
torpedoes up to the lower hangar deck, via the torpedo
workshop on the tween deck. The after magazine spaces
for aircraft ordnance could stow 80–90 torpedoes or 220
mines with a normal stowage of 66 torpedoes and 48
mines. No provision appears to have been made for
bombing-up on the flight deck except by cross transfer
via the aircraft lifts.

ARMOUR PROTECTION
The ship's main vertical protection consisted of a
100mm waterline belt 4m (13ft 1in) deep extending
from frame 57 to frame 177 (ie about 48 per cent of the
waterline length) covering the machinery spaces and
after magazines. Forward, this belt was reduced to
60mm (2⅜in) in the way of the forward 150mm
magazines and then continued to the bows as 40mm
(1⅝in), finally 30mm (1⅛in). Aft, the belt reduced only
to 80mm (3⅛in) to the stern as protection for the steering gear. Inboard of the main vertical belt was a secondary 20mm longitudinal bulkhead which served as a
torpedo bulkhead. The main horizontal armour on the
tween deck was 40mm (1⅝in) thick, with the periphery
increased in thickness to 60mm (2⅜in) and inclined at 45
degrees to join the lower side of the waterline belt.
Closing off the armoured carapace so formed were
transverse armoured bulkheads, 80mm (3⅛in) thick.
Above the steering gear, 60mm (2⅜in) horizontal plate
was employed. No protection was given to the hangar
sides, other than splinter protection but the flight deck
itself was given a degree of protection. This was predo-
minantly 20mm but thickened adjacent to the lift shafts,
especially the centre one where it was 38mm (1½in). This
was undoubtedly for structural strength as well as for
protective reasons. Around the funnel uptakes, the
flight deck was 40mm whilst the vertical uptake protection was 80mm (3⅛in). Other armouring was spread
rather thinly, the casemates having 30mm (1⅛in), flak
directors 14mm and bridge control positions 17mm (³/
₈in) protection. Total weight of armouring was approximately 5000 tonnes.

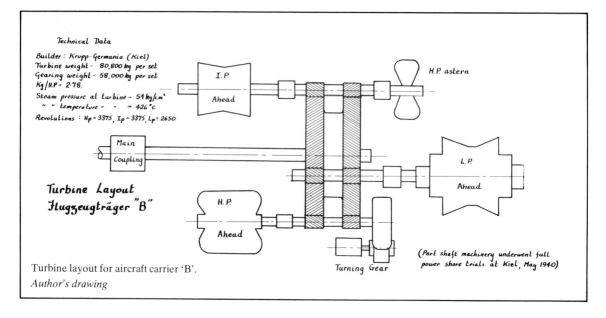

Technical Data

Builder : Krupp-Germania (Kiel)
Turbine weight - 80,800 kg per set
Gearing weight - 58,000 kg per set
Kg/H.P = 2·78.
Steam pressure at turbine = 54 kg/cm²
"   " temperature - - = 426 °C
Revolutions : Hp = 3375, Ip = 3375, Lp = 2650

Turbine Layout
Flugzeugträger "B"

(Port shaft machinery underwent full power shore trials at Kiel, May 1940)

Turbine layout for aircraft carrier 'B'.

Author's drawing

MACHINERY

The steam plant comprised 16 La Mont high pressure boilers, four in each of four boiler rooms. Each boiler, operating steam pressure 70kg/cm² at 450°C, had a rated capacity of 70 tonnes per hour and was equipped with two Saake ring oil burners, both at one end of the furnace under automatic Askania control. Economisers and air-preheaters were fitted, with forced circulation for which an efficiency of 85 per cent was claimed. Although these boilers were never to steam at sea aboard the carrier, they were basically similar to those aboard *Admiral Hipper* class heavy cruisers and would have undoubtedly suffered the same problems in service. Troubles experienced with the circulating pump and overheating of the air pre-heaters were eventually overcome but excessive corrosion of the superheaters caused by a carry over of 1 to 3 per cent continued despite alterations to the baffling in the steam drum. Corrosion also occurred in the economisers but the generator tubes themselves were relatively trouble free. The boilers for Aircraft Carrier 'A' were built by Deutschewerk, Kiel, those for 'B' by Germaniawerft.

The geared turbine installation had a designed power of 50,000hp per shaft on a four shaft arrangement, in three separate turbine rooms. The forward turbine room housed two turbine sets driving the wing shafts whilst the centre and aft turbine rooms contained the inner starboard and port turbines respectively. The turbines differed slightly between the two ships scheduled to be built, although initially both were to be identical. Those for *'Flugzeugträger A'* consisted of Brown Boverie & Co impulse/reaction type cruising and high pressure stages with straight reaction type intermediate turbines. Astern power was provided by a stern element in the forward end of the IP turbine, separated from the ahead blading by a diaphragm, whilst the astern element of the LP (low power) turbine was a double flow reaction stage at the centre of the casing. Like all German turbine designs, separate casings were employed for each turbine stage due to the retention of single reduction (double helical) gearing, leading to layouts which were extremely wasteful in terms of weight and space. Efficiencies too were generally low.

The turbines for 'B' were built by Germania and were somewhat modified, being similar to those of *Prinz Eugen* except that the astern element in the IP turbine was removed and installed as a separate Curtis wheel on the forward end of the IP pinion. Comb type disengaging couplings were fitted to each shaft and could be operated at speeds up to 18 knots by synchronising turbine speed with trailing shaft speed.

Four boilers for *'Flugzeugträger B'* had been completed by Germaniawerft at Kiel and underwent trials before 'B' was cancelled. The electrical generating capacity of the design incorporated four generator rooms using both turbo- and diesel generation. These were distributed as follows:

Generator Room	Location	Diesel	Turbo
No 1	No 1 Turbine Rm Upper Platform dk Stb		2 × 460kw
No 2	No 2 Turbine Rm Upper Platform dk Pt	2 × 350kw	2 × 460kw
No 3	Lower Platform dk Pt amidships		1 × 460kw 1 × 230kw
No 4	Fwd of No 4 BR Lower platform dk Pt	2 × 350kw	

AC power for control circuits, particularly gunnery fire control, was provided by one 400kw converter and four 100kw sets, the 400kw vertical type motor alternator being in No 2 generator room.

Harbour steam supplies were provided by a separate auxiliary boiler room to starboard of No 4 generator space.

The main engine control stand and damage control centre was on the upper platform deck between No 3 turbine room and No 1 boiler room. Damage control arrangements were comprehensive, with the hull being divided into 21 watertight compartments. For fire fighting purposes, besides the sea water lines supplied by the main hull and fire pumps, and steam drenching, there were 20 gaseous extinguisher units that could flood compartments with 'Ardixine' gas to smother fire. This was not without its own hazards however, for it would also asphyxiate the crew and moreover could seep unnoticed through defective glands and seals into adjacent mess decks. This in fact occurred aboard *Admiral Hipper* when a number of men were found dead in their hammocks the following morning after firefighting activities the previous evening in nearby spaces.

An interesting feature of the propulsion plant was the provision of two Voigt-Schneider propeller rudders to assist berthing of the ship in harbour. These two units, powered by 450kw DC electric motors were installed in the fore-ends on the centre line and could be withdrawn through watertight doors in the ship's bottom when not in use. They could exert a lateral impulse of 7.7 tonnes and whilst not intended for use at sea, could, in emergency, be used for steering purposes at speeds not exceeding 12 knots, Furthermore, in the event of the main engines being destroyed, a speed of 3 to 4 knots could be obtained by using them to propel the ship.

The bunker capacity as designed was 5000 tonnes oil fuel, which calculations showed to be sufficient for an endurance of about 9600 miles at 19.1 knots steaming on two shafts (4 boilers) with 10,500hp each. At normal full power of 42,000hp per shaft and 16 boilers on line, a speed of 35.25 knots and an endurance of approximately 3020 miles was anticipated. However, practical results on ships in service with similar power plants later showed that the designed endurance figures for all classes of *Kriegsmarine* warships were wildly optimistic. This was due to several reasons. First, the calculations included only the minimum number of boilers flashed up to make the desired speed and ignored the need to keep part of the powerplant at short notice for steam under war conditions. Second, for stability reasons, many ships could not consume all fuel stowed. Third, in service, many of the high speed steam-driven auxiliary turbines were extremely avaricious consumers of steam and grossly inefficient. (This was particularly true of the Type 39 torpedo boats for example.) Thus it is unlikely that the endurance figures obtained on shore trials and design calculations given below would have been achieved in service:

Speed (kts)	36.5	24.2	19.15	15.3	15.3
Shafts (hp)	4×50,000	4×10,500	4×5000	4×2500	2×5500
Endurance	2645nm	6750nm	8340nm	8800nm	11,480nm

ARMAMENT

The disposition and type of the main gun armament was, as has been noted earlier, outdated. Not only were the 150mm guns suitable only for low angle use but the casemate installation would also probably have led to their being washed out in a seaway, particularly the forward mountings. British, Japanese and US carriers had by this time dispensed with low angle guns, relying on their escort to provide anti-ship defence. This continued use of separate L/A and H/A guns was common German practice at the time however and was also to be seen in the *Bismarck* class. Indeed it was even included in the designs of their successors. As far as German ships were concerned, it absorbed much extra weight and space, which could have been better employed elsewhere. By the time that the British, US and Japanese trends had become known, it would have been impossible to rework the design but the 150mm guns could and might well, have been omitted on entry into service and the weight saved used to augment the heavy flak.

Main fire control was exercised by means of the 7m rangefinder atop the bridge in conjunction with two director sights in the gunnery control stand below it. An auxiliary director sight for astern fire control was fitted immediately abaft the after flak director tower. The transmitting station for the 150mm guns was situated on the lower platform deck, port side, compartment 17. Also in this compartment were the associated amplifier, switch and power rooms.

The heavy flak armament, which consisted of the standard 105mm SK C/33 gun, was carried in twin mountings disposed on the starboard side, fore and aft of the island. Originally, the design incorporated five twin mountings with two forward and three aft but an extra mount was worked in on the flight deck above S2 150mm casemate. Allied with the provision of four tri-axially stabilised 4m base fire control towers, this made for a very respectable A/A outfit, but like the low angle guns, its disposition was open to question. Being all mounted on the starboard side, the engagement of, for example, low flying torpedo bombers approaching from the port beam would have been impossible if the carrier's own squadrons were taking off at the same time. Also, with the guns themselves so closely grouped, one hit could conceivably put 60 per cent of the heavy flak out of action.

Two flak control positions were provided at the fore and after ends of the lower funnel platform, which, in conjunction with the four range-finder towers and two separate flak transmitting stations, one in compartment XII and one forward in the same compartment as the low angle fire control station, provided comprehensive control facilities for air defence. There were however, a number of deficiencies in this system, caused mainly by its over-complicated layout, and poor weather proofing arrangements on the guns and electrical systems. The efficiency of gun installations was reduced by the long heating times for thyratron amplifiers – some three minutes and the use of large gyros for flak director stabilisation also led to long running up periods. Reliability and accessibility too were less than desirable, so that the flak control systems aboard *Scharnhorst* and *Admiral Hipper* with all these problems proved less effective than they might have been. The new carriers were designed with basically the same systems but in view of their scheduled later completion, it is likely that at least some of these deficiencies would have been rectified as was done, for example, with *Admiral Hipper*'s later near sister *Prinz Eugen*, whose flak directors were fitted with small gyro stabilisation and motor follow up giving a consequent decrease in reaction time.

The remainder of the flak outfit consisted of the standard 37mm and 20mm guns in twin and single mountings. A total of 22 37mm SK C/30 guns in twin mountings LC/30 were carried on sponsons around the flight deck, six to port, four to starboard and one on the forecastle. This gun was a hand-worked weapon in a stabilised tri-axial mounting, utilising large gyros, whose potential was limited by some of the defects referred to earlier in the context of gyro-stabilisation. Prototype mountings had not been tested under searching operational conditions with the result that some 300-400 had been built by the time defects became apparent. These were principally associated with poor weather proofing and the failure of the gyro-stabilisation system, 30 1.25m base portable rangefinders were provided for each mounting.

Seven single 20mm MG C/30 guns completed the short-range armament. This gun too was a hand-worked weapon, handicapped by its low rate of fire. Thus the designed armament could be summed up as useful in terms of weight of fire and accuracy but inadequately developed and distributed so that its full potential could not be realised. Nevertheless, in comparison with the British 'barrage fire' pompom and ineffective rifle calibre multiple .5 machine guns, it was a great advance and other combatant powers soon followed the lead to larger calibres.

AIRCRAFT

The designed aircraft complement was 43 machines whose types and mix varied through the ship's chequered development. Early drawings show what appear to be wheeled Heinkel He 60 biplanes embarked! Eventually, proposals crystallised into three types for three different missions: Fighter, Bomber, General Purpose (Recce/torpedo/Minelayer).

During the early stages of the carrier's development, *Luftwaffe* (and naval) aircraft were still in the biplane stage as typified by the He 51 and Arado Ar 68 single seat, fixed undercarriage fighters. These were armed with two machine guns and capable of about 306-330km/hr (190-205mph). In the floatplane reconnaissance role was the He 60 two-seat biplane equipped for catapult duty aboard the *Panzerschiffe* and light cruisers of the Fleet. With the probability of a true aircraft carrier entering service, companies such as Arado and Fieseler began to develop designs specifically intended for carrier operation. By 1937, the Arado concern, in competition with Fiesler had produced a naval version of the Ar 95, a coastal patrol/reconnaissance// light attack type that had not been accepted for use by the *Luftwaffe*. The navalised model, known as the Ar 95 was a fixed undercarriage two-seat biplane powered by an 880hp BMW radial engine and capable of a speed of

280km/hr. Modifications included a cockpit canopy, arrestor hook and catapult spools. Three prototypes were built but unfortunately the *Luftwaffe* preferred the Fieseler contender, which was faster and possessed a better range.

The Fieseler type, which owed something to the earlier Fi 156 'Storch', was a lean looking biplane of predatory appearance, powered by an in-line 1100hp Daimler-Benz 601B engine. The two-man crew were seated in tandem and, like its rival, given the comfort of a covered cockpit, open at the rear to allow the operation of a rear defensive gun. In the clean condition, ie without bombs or torpedo, the machine could achieve a top speed of 325km/hr (202mph) and it possessed, if anything, even better STOL characteristics than the Fi 156 due to the ailerons and full span automatic leading edge slats on both upper and lower wings. Large trailing edge flaps were incorporated on the lower wings in addition. Its defensive armament was limited to two 7.9mm machine guns but it could also carry a 1000kg bomb or one torpedo. This machine more than met *Luftwaffe* requirements for a carrier-borne torpedo bomber-/reconnaissance aircraft and Fieseler were awarded a control for 12 pre-production models (Fi 167A-0) to follow the two prototypes, (Fi 167 V1 & V2). These pre-production aircraft featured a few refinements and the addition of a dinghy for the crew. A production order did not follow for the carrier herself was suspended in 1940 and the completed machines used for a variety of trials before being formed into *Erprobungsstaffel 167* and posted to the occupied Netherlands for advanced coastal service trials until 1942. When work was resumed on the ship however, it was decided to use a modified Ju 87 (Ju 87E) for the tasks originally intended for the Fi 167 and as a result the surviving nine aircraft were surplus to requirements, being finally sold to Rumania for operations over the Black Sea.

TABLE 1: BOILER DATA	
Boiler design	La Mont
Builder	Krupp-Germania
Boilers per ship	16
Economisers	La Mont
Air pre-heater	Horizontal Streamlined
Normal evaporation	60 tonnes/hr
Maximum evaporation	70 tonnes/hr
Pressure at drum	70kg/cm (Max permissible 75kg/cm)
Temperature at S/H outlet	450°C
Feed water temperature	95°C
Efficiency	82.6%
Boiler heating surface	122 sq m
Superheater surface	146.8 sq m
Economiser surface	366.1 sq m
Air pre-heater surface	486 sq m
Radiant surface	29 sq m
Furnace volume	20.4 cubic m
Boiler width	3830mm
Boiler height	5305mm (to top of steam take-off drum)
Boiler depth	4098mm

Port broadside view of *Graf Zeppelin*, taken at Gotenhafen (Gdynia) in 1941. Note camouflage netting and reasonably good condition of the paintwork.

Drüppel

Arado persevered in the the naval fighter requirement and produced the Ar 197, a single seat fighter which could also carry 200kg (440lb) of light bombs. This design, still a biplane type, had maximum speed of 400km/hr (248mph) and was armed with two machine guns in the fuselage and two 20mm cannon in the upper wings. It was in fact very similar to the Fleet Air Arm's latest fighter, the Sea Gladiator, which entered squadron service in 1937. Unlike the British force however, which had to make do with what it could get hold of, and operated biplanes throughout the war, the *Luftwaffe* intended to go to sea with the best fighter available and it was once again unfortunate for Arado that Professor Messerschmitt had completed the first prototype of the Bf 109 fighter monoplane late in 1935, production versions of which began to enter service in 1937. The age of the biplane was at an end and the new monoplane far eclipsed the Ar 197 performance with the result that only three biplane prototypes were flown and tested before the project was abandoned.

Not surprisingly, the aircraft eventually chosen for the fighter role was the *Luftwaffe*'s premier machine, the Bf 109, modified for naval employment. (Quite whether the *Luftwaffe* would have been so generous if the Navy

TABLE 2: MAIN GUN ARMAMENT

15cm SKC/28k gun in 15cm Dop. LC/36

Calibre	149.1mm
Muzzle velocity	875m/s
Barrel length	55cal/8200mm
Liner length	52.4cal/7816mm
Constructional gas pressure	3050kg/mm²
Barrel life	1100rnds
Recoil force at 0° elevation	52000kg
Weight of breech & barrel	9026kg
Max range	22,000m
Ammunition	
Weight of shell	45.3kg
Weight of charge	14kg
Length of shell	655mm
Weight of cartridge	23.5kg
Length of cartridge	865mm
Mounting	
Elevation/depression	+35°/−10°
Training limits	±360°=720°
Elevation change per handwheel revolution	1.5°
Training change per handwheel revolution	6.0°
Weight of cast gun cradle	5109kg
Weight of base	2800kg
Weight of pedestal	13,620kg
Weight of training gear	892kg
Electric power	1300kg
Weight of shield	8627kg
Total weight of mounting	47,600
Armour	30mm fwd/30 side/ 30 rear
Armour type	Whn/A

TABLE 3: FLAK ARMAMENT

3.7 SK C/30 in twin mounting C/30

Calibre	3.7cm	**Training charge per**	
Muzzel velocity	1000m/s	**handwheel revolution**	4°
Muzzle energy	38mt	**Weight of cradle, brake etc**	
Barrel length	83 cal (3074mm)	(swinging mass)	243kg
Bore length	80cal (2960mm)	**Weight of cast gun cradle**	152.5kg
Constructional gas pressure	3450kg/cm	**Weight of base**	71kg
Barrel life	7500rnds	**Weight of pedestal**	2162kg
Recoil force (0° elevation)	1000kg	**Weight of training gear**	87kg
Length of rifling	2554mm	**Weight of electric power**	630kg
Type of rifling	Cubic parabola 50/35	**Complete mounting**	3670kg
Number of grooves	16	*2cm C/30 in 2cm Pedestal L30*	
Weight of barrel and breech	243kg	**Calibre**	2cm
Max horizontal range	8500m	**Muzzle velocity**	835m/s
Max vertical range	6800m (tracer 4800m)	**Barrel length**	65cal (1300mm)
Construction	Monobloc barrel with	**Bore length**	65cal (1300mm)
	drawn on breech ring.	**Constructional sea pressure**	2800kg/cm²
	Vertical sliding block	**Barrel life**	22,000rnds
	breech. Hydraulic brake	**Recoil force** (0° elevation)	250kg
	and spring recuperator.	**Length of rifling**	720mm
		Weight of barrel and breech	64kg
Ammunition		**Max horizontal range**	4900m
Weight of shell	742kg	**Max vertical range**	3700m
Weight of charge	365kg	*Ammunition*	
HE charge	Fp 02	**Weight of shell**	134g
Length of shell	162mm	**Length of shell**	78.5mm
Weight of cartridge	970kg	**Weight of charge**	39.5g
Length of cartridge	381mm	**Weight of complete round**	320g
Propellant	RPC/32	**Length of complete round**	203mm
Weight of complete round	2.1kg	**Rate of fire**	280rpm cyclic,
Length of complete round	516.5mm		120rpm practical
Fuses	E Nose fuse C/30	**Magazine**	20rnds
	Nose fuse C/34	*Mounting*	
	Ers St C/34 (Tracer)	**Elevation/depression**	+85°/−11°
Duration of tracer	12secs	**Training limits**	none
Rate of fire	160rpm cyclic.	**Weight cradle, brake etc**	
	80rpm practical	(swinging mass)	43kg
Mounting		**Weight of mounting**	
Elevation/depression	+85°/−10°	without sights	282kg
Training limits	±360°=720°	**Weight of complete gun**	420kg
Elevation charge per			
handwheel revolution	3°		

had had an independent air arm is very much open to doubt). Nor were the machines to be obsolete marks – Messerschmitt had been ordered to produce a carrier-borne version of the current Bf 109E (*Emil*), arguably the best version to be produced in the long production period of this famous fighter. Messerschmitt began work on the project and built one pre-production aircraft, designated Bf 109T-0 (the 'T' referring to *Träger* or Carrier) before concentrating on the *Luftwaffe*'s own land-based fighters and turning the project over to the Fieseler aircraft company for final detail design work.

Fieseler were also to produce the production versions. The carrier version was powered by a Daimler-Benz DB601N 12 cylinder engine of 1200hp giving the fighter a maximum speed (at 20,000ft) of 568km/hr (353mph). The 'T' version differed from the *Emil* mainly by the increased wing span achieved by adding about .6m (2ft) to each outer wing panel the provision of folding wings which hinged just outboard of the gun bays. Catapult points and an arrestor hook completed the carrier conversion. Armament comprised two 7.9mm MG 17 machine guns in the fuselage and two more (or 20mm cannon) in the wings. Ten new airframes were transferred from the parent factory production line to Fieseler and completed as T-0s. Later an order was received for a production batch of 60T-Is, the definitive service version. After the suspension of *Graf Zeppelin* the fighter order too was suspended but some time later, production restarted with a modified design, T-2, with catapult points and arrestor hook deleted for land service. These

Detail close-up of her port bow at Gotenhafen. Note the empty casemates and sponsons. At the forward end of the flight deck can be seen the end of the port catapult track.
Archiv Gröner

TABLE 4: NAVAL AIRCRAFT

Arado Ar 197
Type	Single seat naval fighter
Powerplant	One 880hp BMW 132 De radial engine
Performance	Max speed 400km/hr at 2500m
	Cruising speed 355km/hr
	Service ceiling 8000m
	Range 695km
Weights	Empty 1840kg
	Maximum 2475kg
Dimensions	Span 11m, length 9.2m, height 3.6m
Armament	2 fixed 7.9mm MG in fuselage
	2 fixed 2cm cannon in upper wing
	200kg light bombs

Fieseler Fi 167
Type	Carrier-borne torpedo reconnaissance bomber
Powerplant	One 1100hp Daimler-Benz 601B
Performance	Max speed 325km/hr
	Cruising speed 270km/hr
	Service ceiling 8200m
	Range 1500km
Weights	Empty 2800kg
	Maximum 4850kg
Dimensions	Span 13.5m, length 11.40m, height 4.8m
Armament	One fixed forward firing 7.92mm MG17
	One flexible rear firing 7.92mm MG15
	One 1000kg bomb or one 765kg torpedo

Junkers Ju 87B
Type	Carrier-borne dive bomber
Powerplant	One 1200hp Jumo 211B Jumo 211Da
Performance	Max speed 340km/hr (at sea level)
	Cruising speed 282km/hr
	Service ceiling 8000m
	Range 790km
Weights	Empty 2710kg
	Maximum 4340kg
Dimensions	Span 13.8m, length 11.1m, height 4.01m
Armament	2 fixed 7.9mm MG17 in wings
	One flexible 7.9mm MG15 in after cockpit
	500kg of bombs

Ju 87C, the naval version was a modified Ju 87B with slightly higher weights and presumably a little lower performance.

Messerschmitt Bf 109T
Type	Single seat naval fighter
Powerplant	One Daimler Benz DB 601N 1200hp
Performance	Max speed 568km/hr at 6150m
	Cruising speed 483km/hr
	Service ceiling 10,500m
	Range 660km
Weights	Empty 2000kg
	Maximum 2954kg
Dimensions	Span 11.18m, length 10.38m, height 2.6m
Armament	2 × 7.9mm MG17 in fuselage
	2 × 7.9mm MG17 or 2cm cannon in wings

Arado Ar 195
Type	Carrier-borne attack/reconnaissance
Powerplant	One 880hp BMW 132 De radial engine
Performance	Max speed 280km/hr
	Cruising speed 250km/hr
	Service ceiling 6000m
	Range 650km
Weights	Empty 2380kg
	Maximum 3745kg
Dimensions	Span 12.50m, length 10.5m, height 3.6m
Armament	One fixed forward firing 7.9mm MG17
	One flexible rear-firing 7.9mm MG15
	One 800kg torpedo or 500kg bomb

machines were issued for service in Norway, principally with *I Gruppe/Jagdgeschwader 77* where their performance was well suited to the short exposed airstrips typical of that country.

There was only one choice for the bomber role – the Junkers Ju 87 'Stuka', which was to become the standard *Luftwaffe* dive bomber. Entering service with the land-based air force in 1937, the Ju 87 had been sent to Spain for operational testing during the Civil War and had since been honed into a highly effective weapon that was later to symbolise the *Blitzkrieg* of 1939–41. The basis for the naval version was the Ju 87B, modified as the Ju 87C which was fitted with catapult points and manually folding wings. Jettisonable undercarriage facilitated emergency ditching. The pre-production model was designated Ju 87C-0 and the production model JuC-1. In the event the carrier's suspension led to the cancellation of the production order and the majority of the airframes converted to the Ju 7B-2. In 1942, following resumption of work on the ship, a new mark Ju 87E was proposed to combine the tasks of the Ju 87C and Fi 167 but the ship was cancelled again before this version left the drawing board.

Despite the hopes of the *Kriegsmarine* and the grandiose plans of Milch nearly five years earlier, on the outbreak of war in September 1939, only one carrier-borne *grüppe* had formed-*Trägergrüppe 186* at Kiel-Holtenau comprising three *staffeln*, *4/186* equipped with Ju 87s and *5&6/186* with Bf 109s. Nevertheless they *were* available and even if their aircraft were not all fit for sea service, sufficient machines could probably have been scrapped together to send a makeshift *grüppe* to sea. Unfortunately it was the carrier which was missing and in consequence the aircraft were utilised for the land offensive against Poland when the Ju 87s of *4/186* sank the destroyer *Wicher* at Hela on 3 September.

To be continued

The Type II U-boat

By David Westwood

Type IIB U-boats of the 1st U-boat or *Weddigen* Training Flotilla in late 1935. From left to right *U8, U10, U9, U11, U7*. All except *U7* (sunk in collision W of Pillau 18 February 1944) survived World War II only to be scuttled or scrapped afterwards.

When World War II broke out in September 1939, the German Navy possessed 57 U-boats, not all which were operational. Many historians and naval commentators have made much of this total without examining the type and role of the various submarines that made up that figure. In fact 30 of that total were of the Type II class, boats of restricted range (a maximum operational radius of 1500 miles), and limited offensive capability (they carried only five torpedoes or 12 tube-launched mines). However, memories of U-boat warfare in World War I had made other nations in Europe wary of the still new naval weapon, and the effect of propaganda and counter-propaganda at the time are still felt today.

John P Holland had designed his original boats at the turn of the century; during World War I developments of his original craft had wrought havoc against Allied and neutral merchant shipping. Germany saw the value of this new weapon, and had used it to great effect, supplementing surface operations, and later surpassing the more traditional methods.

Submarines, before the advent of nuclear power, were no more than submersibles; they were slow, vulnerable to gunfire, and limited even more when they submerged. But they had one advantage over all their contemporaries – the ability to submerge and so conceal themselves. This was the edge they possessed, and in the words of Wilhelm Bauer, Germany's first submarine designer, this reduced the battleships to '*Eisenkolosse*' or simply iron lumps with no future. But the U-boat's strategic role lay not in attacking and sinking warships but in cutting the economic lifeline which stretches some 3000 miles across the Atlantic between Europe and the Americas. It was in this field that the German submarine effort was eventually concentrated in the course of both World Wars, and which nearly cost the Allies the decision – twice.

THE UB II PREDECESSOR
Due to the limitations then inherent in submarine design, the original operational role of these craft had

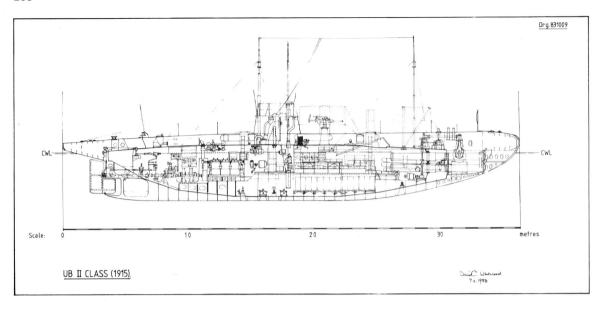

Drg. 831009

CWL —— CWL

Scale: 0   10   20   30   metres

UB II CLASS (1915).

David C. Westwood
7.x.1983

been seen as local, coastal patrols, with the occasional foray into enemy patrolled waters to lay ambush to traffic at nodal points, especially the entrances to harbours. The range restrictions of the early boats combined with their limited arament to produce boats of very reduced tactical value. The predecessor of the Type II U-boat was the World War I Type UB II design, ordered and built after the war had started. Its characteristics were typical of a coastal U-boat. In 1915, when the boats began to commission, German Navy submarine operations were being carried out off Flanders and elsewhere in the North Sea, and so the limitations of the boats had no serious effect. Longer range operations in the Atlantic were not then in full swing, and were to be carried out by larger boats, specifically designed for that purpose.

The UB II design was built by two constructors: Blohm & Voss, Hamburg, and A G 'Weser', Bremen. Thirty of the class were built, the first of them (UB 18) commissioning on 11 December 1915. The last of the class was accepted by the German Navy on 4 July 1916. (A comparison between the main characteristics of this class and the later Type II boats will be found at Appendix A). All UB II boats had twin 6-cylinder diesels, two electric motors and 122 battery cells. They were an improvement on the earliest German designs, and had twin hydroplanes fore and aft but they had only single propeller and rudder arrangements.

They were fitted with two 500mm (19.7in) torpedo tubes forward, arranged vertically, to improve the bow line of the boat. Some were also fitted with two lattice torpedo release tubes between tower and deck gun, above the waterline. In this latter case the internal tubes were modified to fire P-mines, of which 14 were carried; this was to allow the U-boat to carry out its secondary task of minelaying. There was also either a 50mm or 88mm gun, forward of the tower. The general

opinion of the boat was that it was adequate for its limited task, but was not a good sea-going vessel.

During the First World War, of the 30 boats of the class 17 were lost to enemy action or other cause off Flanders, 2 were lost elsewhere in the North Sea; 6 were lost in the Mediterranean, and 5 were used solely for training, and scrapped after the war. They did not contribute anything of great importance to the German submarine effort between 1915 and 1918, but served as an example of how quickly a small coastal U-boat could be designed and built. The boats built by Blohm &

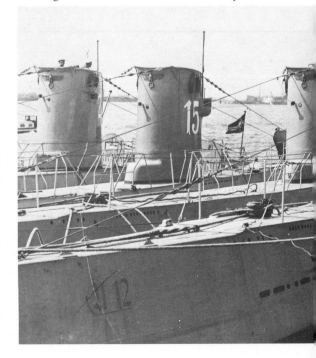

Voss, for example, were laid down and completed as follows:

Boat numbers	Date ordered	Date launched
UB 18 - 23	30.4.15	21.8.15 - 9.10.15
UB 30 - 41	22.7.15	16.11.15 - 6.5.16

(A maximum of ten months from order to launch.) This exercise was to be repeated in the case of the Type II boats 20 years later.

BETWEEN THE WARS

The war lost for Germany, the victorious Allies decided that the losers had to pay for the cost. The Treaty of Versailles was imposed upon Germany. Articles 188, 189 and 191 ruled that Germany was to have no submarines at all, and that any remaining boats were to be delivered to the victors; further, boats already in construction were to be destroyed as they lay. The sword was being turned into the ploughshare with a vengeance. This was further reinforced by the direction that all equipment and machinery formerly used for warship construction was to be converted at once to making trade goods.

The prohibition by the Treaty was total with regard to submarines, and the general effects of it were swinging. There can be little doubt that the Treaty conditions and French insistence that Germany maintain reparation payments, especially as the 1920s drew to a close were factors in the rise and power of Hitler and the Nazi party. Hitler came into power in January 1933; what had the designers and builders of U-boats been doing from 1922 to that date?

What they had not been doing was observing the strict letter of the Versailles Treaty. Although they had not flouted the Treaty openly, for that would have led to confiscations and sanctions, they had conspired to establish a commercial design firm, based in the Hague. Other design work was also done – abroad – particularly by Hans Techel in Kobe (Japan), designs which served as the basis for the later *I 1-3* and *21-24* boats. Interestingly enough, in Germany, it was a request from Argentina that led to the Hague firm being established. The Argentine Government asked the German Navy to design and build ten submarines for them.

The boats were to be built in Argentina, but the designs were to be wholly German, reflecting their importance and experience in the field. Krupp, one of Europe's largest armament manufacturers, was naturally involved, because the colossal conglomerate owned the yards of Germaniawerft at Kiel and A G 'Weser' in Bremen. In concert with the German Navy, Krupp decided that the way to circumvent the Treaty was to set up a commercial submarine design firm. This was *N V Ingenieurskaantor vor Scheepsbouw (IvS),* established in the Hague under the command of Dr Techel, newly returned from Kobe.

Up to January 1933, *IvS* designed submarines for no fewer than 19 foreign countries, producing plans for 86 boats. Further, they had the satisfaction of seeing nine of these designs launched and commissioned. These were two designs for Turkey; one each for Spain, Sweden, Russia and Rumania, and three designs for Finland (5 boats in all were built).

It is with the last country, Finland, that the most effective work was done, leading to the Type II design.

CV 707 DESIGN FOR FINLAND

Finland first expressed interest in submarines to *IvS* in 1924, needing a design for a 100-ton minelayer. The Finns soon realised that the designed boat was rather small, even for limited operations in Lake Ladoga, so they asked for a larger boat to be brought out. (The small boat was completed and saw service in the Finnish Navy, having the distinction of being the then smallest submarine in service in the world.) But the larger design, CV 707 as it was known to *IvS*, of 250 tons planned displacement, was acceptable both to the Finns and eventually to the newly established *Kriegsmarine.*

The CV 707 was a more practical boat than the smaller *Saukko* (Pr 110 to *Ivs*). She displaced 248/297 tons, and had a range of 1500 miles. (No saddle-tanks were fitted initially, but see below for the incorporation of extra fuel capacity by this means.) Interestingly, her three bow torpedo tubes, now of 533m calibre (21in), were arranged in an 'eyes and mouth' layout, increasing her firepower by 50 per cent over UB II boats, yet retaining a practical bow form. She had clean, attractive lines, and an altogether seaworthy appearance. The three boats Finland commissioned were constructed in

Ten Type II boats in 1935, including *U2, U15, U16, U12, U14, U20* and others of the 'Weddigen' Flotilla with astern of *U14,* their new depot ship *Saar.*
Drüppel/courtesy of M J Whitley

Finnish yards, but under German supervision; needless to say the German Navy kept a close eye on progress, with a view to making the decision whether to use the design if Germany were once more to have a submarine arm.

During the later 1920s and early 1930s the German Navy spent much time evaluating the next submarine family, as well as looking at modern designs for surface ships. Admiral Erich Raeder had been appointed Commander-in-Chief of the Navy in 1928, and his firm view was that Germany, having to build from scratch, would have to have a balanced navy of sufficient strength to enable her to fulfil her continental defensive role at least. Part of that balanced navy would be the submarine arm, and to the officers and technologists of that arm could get experience abroad which would later serve the new arm well. So it was that many of the personnel concerned with submarines, before Germany actually had any, spent a lot of time in Finland (and elsewhere), testing the *Vesikko* (as CV 707) was later named by the Finnish Navy. At this time the Navy became so involved in the commercial enterprise that another camouflaged organisation was established, within the Navy itself, called *Igewit*, which coordinated the efforts of the commercial and military interests.

While CV 707 was building numerous Germans,

apparently retired naval officers, arrived in Finland to observe and take part in the process. Needless to say, they all had official backgrounds, and were there simply to glean all the information they could. The Finnish Government did not seem to mind; indeed, so courteous were they to the German submarine builders that CV 707, launched on 10 May 1933, underwent sea trials under German supervision, and was not handed over to the Finns until 13 January 1936. She saw service from then to the end of Finnish participation in World War II, and is now laid up at Suomenlinna/Sveaborg in Finland.

The tacit approval of this Treaty avoiding activity was not limited to Finland. A similar situation existed in Turkish and Spanish dealings with *IvS*, and therefore indirectly with the German Navy. New political alliances were being formed, and the European treaty map was once more being redrawn. In recognition of this, but paying lip-service to the Versailles Treaty, the German Navy under Raeder planned ahead for the future fleet. The new government under Hitler, and the voting of special powers to it by the Reichstag on 24 March 1933, meant the hope that plans would become reality had a firm chance of realisation.

Raeder wrote after the war that Chancellor von Papen and the new German Government felt that

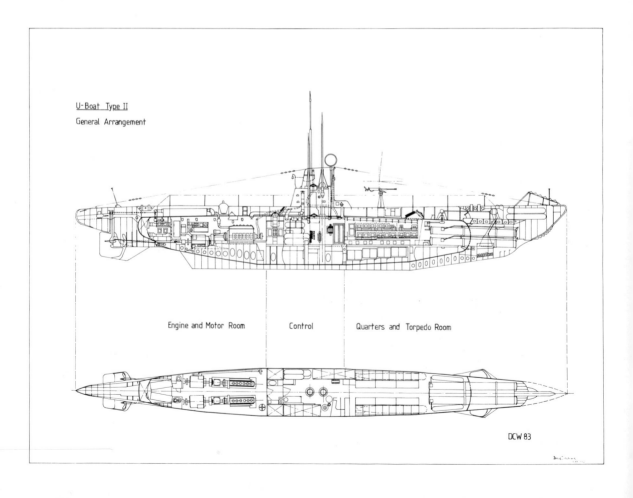

U-Boat Type II
General Arrangement

Engine and Motor Room   Control   Quarters and Torpedo Room

DCW 83

The Type IIB boat *U18* in smart pre-war paintwork at Kiel, rigged for surface running.
Drüppel/courtesy of M J Whitley

'small circumventions of the Versailles Treaty disarmament conditions were entirely permissible in the light of the international situation'. But the main problem lay with the attitudes of the supervising powers (Great Britain, France, Italy and Russia) rearmament on a scale far beyond the needs of defence, and especially the possession by Germany of a modern navy and the specifically prohibited U-boats. To free Germany from the restrictions of that Treaty in one unilateral move was not then politically possible, but the Germans felt that if they could convince Great Britain that they did not want parity with the Royal Navy, but would in fact impose limitations upon themselves as to the size and composition of the *Kriegsmarine,* then they might escape the shackles of Versailles by steps.

The Anglo-German Naval Treaty was, from start to finish, merely a discussion on how to present the German proposals to the world. Von Ribbentrop and his envoys opened the conference with the Foreign Office and Admiralty representatives by saying that if the British did not agree to Germany having 35 per cent of the tonnage of the Royal Navy except submarines, when they were to have 45 per cent, they were under instructions to return to Germany. The conference eventually endorsed the German proposal, as well as the further proviso that should Germany ask, the British were bound to agree to an increase in submarine tonnage to parity with the Royal Navy. This London Naval Agreement was signed in 1935, and the London Submarine Agreement (governing the conduct of submarine warfare) just over a year later. But it was the 1935 Treaty that gave Germany the *de jure* right to disregard the terms of the Versailles Treaty, and to build and commission submarines once more.

Raeder was against war with England. He said in his autobiography that in the First World War 'it was British and American seapower that brought us to our knees despite the great victories on land and the Russian breakdown' and his pre-war aim was that 'Such a situation should never be allowed to recur'. He intended, above all, to avoid conflict with Great Britain, and to build a new, ultra-modern navy that would be able to hold out against the navies of Germany's neighbours to the west and east – France and Poland.

TYPE II EMERGES

This permission to re-enter the submarine field did not, of course, surprise the German Navy, especially the so-called Anti-Submarine School (cover name for the embryo submarine arm). Once the 1935 Treaty had been signed, Germany immediately went ahead with the final construction of the U-boats that had been ordered months before the meetings in London took place. The first boats ordered and built for the new navy were of the Type II Class, designed on the basis of the UB II, and modified and improved by the experience gained in Finland through *IvS*. At the same time Type IA and early versions of the Type VII boats were also under construction.

Raeder now planned to get as many Type II boats into service as he could (within the agreed tonnage), and in the shortest possible time. The simplicity of the boats, and past experience helped, and he had a training flotilla and a service flotilla established before the end of 1935. The man he chose to command the 1st (*Weddigen*) U-boat Flotilla (and then the whole submarine service) was Captain Karl Dönitz.

The Type II was really no more than a refined version of the CV 707 design, and the first of the class *UI* was launched on 15 June 1935, and commissioned only 14 days later. Together with *U2-6* she went to the 1st Training Flotilla to form the basis of this new German U-boat Arm. By 28 September of that year the 1st U-boat Flotilla became reality, for *U7-9* arrived at their base, soon to be followed by another nine boats, *U10-18*.

As Dönitz wrote, after the war, the boat was 'A very simple and successful vessel, but very small'. As can be seen from the plans, the boat was little larger than the UB II design. But the reduced displacement of these boats meant that more of them could be built within the tonnage permitted by the London Naval Agreement than could be built of the larger 500- and 750-ton vessels. It also meant that the U-boat Arm would achieve a high strength in units, even if not in actual fighting power.

In all there were four versions of the Type II. The first, Type IIA, was the basis for development, and was like the initial *Vesikko* in having no saddle-tanks. This was modified in the other three versions of the Class (Types IIB, C and D), and the range of the boats was ultimately increased to 5650 miles. The operational area foreseen for these boats was the Baltic, the North Sea and the French waters of the English Channel. It had no future in the Atlantic, and indeed at the time there seemed no prospect for U-boat employment there anyway. The boats therefore, with their limits in range and firepower seemed insignificant to the British, providing no threat to the Royal Navy, especially as developments in Asdic seemed to reduce the submarine to impotence.

The most important function these boats were to perform was in fact not in the operational, but in the training sphere. Each Type II could be used to train crew after crew of new submariners for the German Navy, who would then progress to conversion courses on the larger Type IA, VII and IX U-boats. As early as 1936 Dönitz had realised that the Type II was 'too weak as regards armament, radius of action and speed'; equally disturbing was the fact that the Type IA was not coming up to expectations either, having an alarming tendency to go for the bottom, no matter what steering orders were passed. However, the Type II building programme continued, for the training function was essential in any event. Slowly U-boat tonnage approached the allowed tonnage under the Anglo-German Naval Agreement.

The class was built in fact until the last two boats were launched in January 1941 (*U151* and *152*), but by then it was obvious that the strategic naval battle was being fought far beyond the range of these little boats. In all three builders (Deutsche Werke and Germaniawerft at Kiel, and Flender-Werft of Lübeck) launched 50 Type II boats. Some were operational in the early part of the war, others renewed their operational careers after a spell training in the Baltic, but the majority remained there, forming the training flotillas of the U-boat Training Units throughout the war. There were still Type II boats to be scuttled after the German capitulation in 1945, so the little boats made a contribution above the average.

CHARACTERISTICS

In the 90ft of the pressure hull there had to be squeezed three officers and 25 men, stores and consumables for up to three weeks on patrol. The hull already had two 6-cylinder MWM diesels and two SSW electric motors. To fuel the diesels there were nearly 12 tons of diesel oil inboard, as well as 62 battery cells beneath the forward compartment to provide underwater power for the electric motors. Two reserve torpedoes (or a number of mines) also had to be fitted in. There was little, if any, spare room in the boat.

There were three main compartments, with watertight doors and bulkheads between them. The forward compartment combined torpedo room, crew's quarters and battery space. Aft lay the control room and the attack centre (located in the tower above the control room). There the officers had their quarters, along with the boat's main controls and the radio room. Finally in the stern was the diesel electric room, housing engines and motors, gearing, shafts and electrical controls, and a minute machine-shop.

Externally the boats had a very low silhouette making the vessels almost invisible at night. The saddle-tanks broadened the hull overall cross-sections, but did not affect performance greatly. The design was undoubtedly suited to short-range patrol work in inshore waters and inland waters; nevertheless in the last days of peace some of the boats were stationed as sea well outside their intended operational areas. The shortages in numbers of the German Navy were critically obvious in the last quarter of 1939. The Type II boats were, then, up to the eve of war, 'political' boats in the sense that they increased numbers, but their fighting capacity was not that great. But they did serve as the backbone of the training side of the U-boat Arm for many years, and made a very important contribution to the eventual effectiveness of Dönitz's force when the Battle of the Atlantic began in earnest.

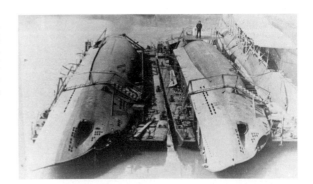

Two Type II boats stripped and pontooned for transit (their port and centre line torpedo tubes show to advantage) to the Black Sea in 1942. The lefthand boat is believed to be *U9* whilst the other is probably *U24*. Alongside is a third boat with camouflage screening above the hull, whose identity is uncertain. She does not appear to by a Type II and is possibly a captured enemy boat (the shape of her stern is distinctive).
Drüppel/courtesy of M J Whitley

Japanese'Kaibokan' Escorts Part 2

By Hans Lengerer and Tomoko Rehm-Takahara

TYPE A, ETOROFU CLASS

More than four years passed before coast defence ships were again included in a building programme. At the liaison conference between the government and the Imperial Headquarters on 2 July 1941 the 'fundamentals of a national policy for the Japanese Empire in consideration of the altered situation' was agreed; this document emphasised strongly the need to push towards the South, and the inevitability of a war with the USA and Britain. In pursuance of this policy, and in recognition of Japan's great inferiority compared with the potential of the USA, the Navy decided to accelerate war production. As early as 15 August 1941 the complete execution of the 'emergency preparation programme' *(Shusshi junbi keikaku)* was decided. Even before that, on 28 July 1941, the 'rapid warship building programme for 1941' *(Showa 16 nendo senji kyuzo kansen senzo keikaku)* had been pushed through as part of this programme. This programme, known as the 'most urgent programme' *(Maru kyu keikaku)*, was aimed at strengthening the numbers of ships designed for defensive duties. It provided for the construction of 288 ships (actually 326, as the supplementary programme also officially belonged to the *Maru kyu keikaku*; among that number were 30 *Kaibokan*, with

Etorofu in May 1943.
CPL

building numbers 310–339. Fourteen units were to be Type A of 860 tons, and 16 ships to be Type B of 940 tons standard displacement, although in the budget all 30 ships were again stated to be of 1200 tons standard displacement; they were to cost 5,112,000 Yen (£513,756) per ship, or 153,360,000 Yen (£1,610,280) in total, 4260 Yen (£451) per ton.

When we consider that at this time Japan only possessed four ships of the *Shimushu* class for escort duties (the destroyers were intended for screening heavy ships) a figure of 30 *Kaibokan* appears to be more than a slight miscalculation: this figure exposes the total ignorance about the need to protect merchant shipping during a war. The Admiralty staff simply failed to recognise the significance of the escort ship, although the battle in the Atlantic made its importance quite obvious.

Although the Type A ships (*Etorofu* class) were allotted the primary role of convoy escort, and the secondary task of minesweeping, the Admiralty staff again demanded only 19.7 knots as top speed, three 120mm (4.7in) guns and one depth-charge thrower. Defence against aircraft and effective anti-submarine work could not be achieved with this armament.

In order not to delay the start of work on the 14 ships, the plans of the *Shimushu* class were adopted and

The Type A *Etorofu* class Kaibokan *Oki* leaving Uraga for final trials on 25 March 1943.

Author's collection

altered only slightly in spite of their complicated structure, which was not suitable for wartime mass-production. For this reason *Etorofu* class ships exhibited scarcely any differences from their predecessors. The alteration of the plans (basic planning number E 19) principally concerned simplification of the bow area, the stern, and the superstructure. The main dimensions were virtually identical, except that the overall length was shortened by 0.30m, due to the new bow shape, and the stardard displacement was increased by 10 tons to 870 tons at the same trials displacement.

The differences from the *Shimushu* class were as follows:

1 The bow was altered to a straight stem with a small overhang. The steel cables of the paravane gear were no longer led through holes in the fore foot, as on the *Shimushu* class, but were routed in roughly the same way as in German warships. The Japanese Navy decided to do this for the first time, because this design, in which the cables were held in outriggers at a pre-determined depth, fixed at the bow and projecting out in the line of travel, was simpler.

2 The bridge no longer projected forward over the lower structure. The cladding consisted of thin steel plates, which protected the crew from machine gun and light machine cannon fire. The open rear extension of the bridge was extended to the forward tripod mast, which was connected to the lower structure by means of supports.

3 The ships completed by about June 1943 had the same forward tripod mast as on the *Shimushu* class, but on later ships it ended just above the 3m (9ft 10in) rangefinder in a platform, on which the aerial of a Type 22 radar was mounted. The topmast now only carried two yards.

4 The radio direction finder was fitted on the searchlight platform behind the searchlight.

5 The upper part of the funnel was no longer tapered, but had the same cross-section over its whole height.

6 The tripod mainmast was longer.

7 The stern was no longer raked aft but straight.

8 Instead of a semi-balanced rudder, a fully balanced rudder was used, and the shape of the stern underwater was simplified. This measure, in conjunction with the altered stern shape, reduced the turning circle and increased the speed.[7]

9 Instead of 18 depth charges, 36 of the Model 95 charges were carried.

10 The anti-submarine electronics consisted of a Model 93 sonar and a Model 93 hydrophone.[8]

Although minesweeping remained part of the ships' duties as before, some of the ships were only equipped with two paravanes, because of the increase in depth charge load to 60 units, which was decided on during the building period. The AA weapons were strengthened and radar fitted as on the *Shimushu* class. On a few ships, however, the number and position of the AA weapons differed somewhat from the standard equipment after the Battle of the Philippine Sea (five triple 25mm); for example, *Kanju* had only two 120mm AA guns in single mounts, but 21 25mm machine guns (5 triples, 2 twins, 2 single mounts) to compensate.

As a result of the simplified design, the building time for the hull was reduced to 70,000 man-days. Even after these alterations the ships were by no means suitable for mass-production and the building time was too long for the hopes of the naval design office to be realised. Moreover, actual war experience made it clear that a specialist escort ship had to be more closely matched to her tasks in terms of armament and equipment. These considerations led to the suspension of building work.

The *Etorofu* class comprised 14 ships, begun between February 1942 and August 1943, and completed between March 1943 and February 1944. During the war eight of them were sunk.

TYPE B, MIKURA CLASS

Together with the 14 ships of the *Etorofu* class, 16 ships of a new class of *Kaibokan* were included in the 'urgent war programme'. The Admiralty staff demanded for the first time an adequate AA and ASW armament:
1 120mm AA as main armament.
2 Two sonar units and 2 hydrophones.
3 Four depth charge throwers and 120 depth charges.
4 One pair of large minesweeping devices *(Tankan shiki sokaigu)*.
5 Speed of 19.7 knots.
6 Range of 5000 miles at 16 knots.

Planning of this type was begun at the beginning of 1942. At first it was intended to be a completely new design, but after further studies it was decided to adopt the *Etorofu* class hull, although in somewhat simplified form, to save time. The principle was to alter neither the displacement[9] nor the shape, but to undertake any possible simplifications in hull construction, because the ships were now to be used exclusively as escort vessels, and no longer as guardships for the North Pacific. In addition, the armament was to be matched more closely to the ships' intended role. The design drawings were therefore completed in a relatively short time (basic planning number E 20), and the ships of the *Etorofu* and *Mikura* classes were built alongside each other.

The differences compares with the *Etorofu* class consisted basically of structural simplifications and alterations of the armaments and equipment.
1 The reinforcement of the hull along the waterline was dropped.
2 Instead of the double floor, the plate thickness was increased, the joints between plates mostly welded, and

The Type B *Mikura* at Tsurumi, Yokohoma as completed at the end of October 1943. She had Type 22 radar on her mainmast and high angle 120mm guns.

an electric welding process was used for the bulkheads and frames.
3 The oil-fired auxiliary boilers were not installed, as the ships were no longer intended for use in the North Pacific.
4 Accommodation, especially the officers' quarters, was considerably simplified; this could be done because by this time the coast defence ships were no longer rated as major warships. The number of scuttles in the area of the lower deck was also reduced as a result of battle experience.
5 While the *Etorofu* and *Shimushu* classes could be said to have a box-type bridge (with some limitations), the form of the *Mikura* class was closer to the form of a stepped bridge, with the front part projecting as far as the forecastle deck, and a high bulwark around the 3m range finder.
6 The superstructure deck was no longer full-length, but divided into two deckhouses.
7 The tripod foremast was the same shape as *Etorofu* class ships completed after about June 1943. The legs had a less severe rake, while the platform carrying the Type 22 radar unit aerial was slightly different, and the method of fixing of the topmast and its rake were slightly different.
8 The radio direction finder was set up in front of the searchlight on the deckhouse.
9 The 75cm searchlight was located on a small, round structure on the deckhouse.
10 The engine rooms and the funnel were moved further aft. The funnel was narrower and thinner, and the galley funnel was led upwards along the forward side.
11 The tripod mainmast was moved further aft, was longer, and upright. The relative distance between the masts was slightly increased by this alteration.
12 The fuel supply was reduced from 200 to 120 tons, with a corresponding drop in range from 8000 miles to 5000 miles at the same speed of 16 knots.
13 Instead of the three 120mm low angle guns in type G mounts, three 120mm/45 AA of the Year 10 model

(10 nendo shiki) were installed. A single mount with shield was located on the forecastle abaft the breakwater as on previous types, while a twin mount without shield was fitted on the quarterdeck.

14 The depth charge load was increased to 120, and the storage rooms in the aftership were arranged below the lower deck. Two Model 94 depth charge throwers with Model 3 loading frames were fitted, along with two depth charge launchers at the stern. The three depth charge launchers situated on either side of the earlier types were omitted. The stern was lengthened by 1.07m (3ft 5in) to fit the larger depth charge rooms.

15 Large minesweeping gear was fitted on a bulge in front of the depth charge launchers on each side. The number of small minesweeping devices (paravanes) was reduced to two. They were again fixed in supports on either side of the superstructure abreast the funnel.

16 The anti-submarine and radar equipment was given due consideration from the outset, and all ships had at least one Model 93 sonar unit when completed, along with one Model 93 hydrophone and one Type 22 radar unit. The newly developed sonar Model 3 type 2 was fitted to the *Chiburi* first in early 1944[10] (the first Japanese ship to be so equipped).

17 The 6m (20ft) motor boat to starboard, previously fitted behind the 6m cutter, was omitted.

Overall, the *Mikura* class differed markedly from its predecessors, and was in many respects a completely different design. While the *Shimushu* and *Etorofu* classes retained much of the character of a gunboat, this type, with reservation, can be said to be the first real escort vessel fully equipped in terms of armament and equipment for ASW and AA work. The fact that they still retained the substantial minesweeping gear at the stern, as on the minesweepers, is proof, however, that the Admiralty staff had still not abandoned the idea of using these ships for minesweeping, and they had once more allotted to the ships a task which was extraneous to their design. The fitting of 2 depth-charge throwers was not exactly adequate for sinking submarines, and even the AA armament, and especially the light AA (four 25mm machine guns in two twin mounts), was inadequate, and the lack of air warning was a further weak point.

As a result of the simplifications listed above, the building time of the hull was reduced from 70,000 to 57,000 man-days. In spite of the saving of virtually 20 per cent, the building time was still considered to be too long and the design too complex, as the war situation was demanding more and more escort vessels. This fact, together with the weaknesses in equipment and armament, led to the Modified Type B. By this time eight ships[11] had been built; they had been started between October 1942 and September 1943, and completed between October 1943 and May 1944. The new type was the *Ukuru* class, whose thorough-going simplification was planned by all the yards working in cooperation.

Soon after the ships were commissioned a general increase in the AA weapons was carried out; the ships were fitted with ten 25mm machine guns (three triple, one single mount), and thus possessed a total of 14 machine guns. Some ships, which were selected for special duties (submarine hunting groups), were fitted with four additional 25mm machine guns in single mounts. The tripod mainmast, on which the antenna of the (Type 13) air search radar was fitted as of autumn 1944, had to give way to the third triple: it was relocated about 3m farther forward. The arrangement of the machine guns differed only slightly from that of the earlier ships: two twin mounts fitted on platforms on both sides of the bridge: two triples on platforms abreast the funnel; the third triple on the centreline at the rear end of the deck superstructure; the single mount in front of the bridge. On a platform forward of and slightly below this was an 80mm trench mortar. At the stern a Model 94 depth charge thrower and one Model 3 loading frame were added. The new Model 2 (1942) type of depth charge was used from this time onward. Several ships were fitted additionally with the new sonar model 3 type 2. Towards the end of the war the large minesweeping equipment on the quarterdeck was removed.

The *Mikura* class comprised eight ships, five of which were sunk during the war.

MODIFIED TYPE B, UKURU CLASS

During the battles for Guadalcanal, which lasted roughly six months, (August 1942 – February 1943) the Japanese Navy lost many small warships, and the losses among merchant ships also increased greatly. The only means of reversing the trend was to mass-produce escort vessels, in order to patrol the main shipping routes, and to protect the convoys. Early in 1943 the Japanese Navy decided to mass-produce the coast defence ships. With the *Mikura* class as the starting point, a new ship was designed under the basic planning number E 20 B; she differed extensively from the Type B, principally in her hull lines, her equipment and the design and production methods – this was the *Ukuru* class. Basically the ships were a modified and simplified form of the *Mikura* class in which the ASW and AA armament had been strengthened, and the structure of the hull simplified as far as possible.

To this end, studies were made of the absolute simplifications that had been carried out since the end of 1942 in merchant shipbuilding and which were to be introduced for the first time in warship building. Although the alterations to the design plans were completed in less than 2 months (April to end of May 1943), and all possible simplifications were included, the first ship, the *Hiburi*, completed on 27 June 1944, nevertheless gave very satisfactory results, and even the speed hardly suffered compared with the *Mikura* class. Indeed, a greater loss of speed had not been expected, in spite of the considerable doubts which had been expressed initially, as the Technical Research Office *(Gijutsu kenkyusho)* had found by experiments involving model ships that there would be hardly any increase in drag even with simplified shapes and at maximum speed (if the same block coefficient as on the earlier ships were retained). At cruising speed the drag was increased by 5 per cent. This shape of hull was also used on the Type D destroyers (*Matsu* class and especially *Tachibana* class) and the first class transports *(Itto Yusokan)* as well as the coast defence ships of Types C and D.

The differences between Type B, the *Mikura* class, and the modified Type B, the *Ukuru* class, were essentially as follows:

1 In order to permit construction of the ships in sections, the shape of the hull was simplified as far as the limits of practicality allowed. The aim was to minimise the use of shaped steel, of which there was already a shortage, and curved plates, and to use those shapes and material thicknesses which were already used in the construction of the standard merchant ships being built. Instead of the rivetted joints used until then, welding was to be extended even to those joints which provided the basic strength of the hull. The increase in the straight and flat, the reduction of the curved, and the virtually complete omission of double-curvature plates (horizontal and vertical), resulted in ribs which were (almost exclusively) either straight or had a single change of direction. The hull consisted now of just flat plates, and single-curved plates joined to them. The time-consuming work of making cast components and forming sheets was considerably reduced.

The adoption of the simplified ship's form dispensed with the overhanging stem of the bow, which became instead a straight definite bow. The forward frames were no longer curved, but entirely straight. The slight change of sheer at the forecastle also began with a

A Type B *Mikura* class Kaibokan in May 1945(?).
Author's collection

sharp angle, which was the typical solution to the direct joining of sheets at different angles. The area where the forecastle deck sheer strake had previously curved gently to meet the deck plates was made perfectly straight, in spite of the potential tension problem, thus producing a further sharp angle between deck and outer plating. The camber of the forecastle deck disappeared; it was made quite flat. The disadvantage of this design was that the water could no longer run off adequately. The odd-looking angle at the step-down of the deck was omitted, the hull sides being flat. The bow lines were fuller, while the transition from the stem to the keel was a simple angle. The earlier elliptical shape of the stern was replaced by a transom stern. The reduction in performance, which in fact was hardly apparent, and the reduced durability, were expected to some extent. Also, bearing in mind the size and fitting out of various compartments, disadvantages and inconveniences had to be accepted, in order to allow more rapid construction.

The officers' and crew's quarters was again simplified, and the single cabins for the officers were replaced by communal areas. These measures did indeed achieve shorter building times and savings in materials, but their effect on operational capability and morale were a major drawback. By contrast with British and American escort ships, habitability was considered a side issue, and from this class onward was terribly neglected. In addition the protective measures against an outbreak of fire or the spreading of fire into other areas of the ship were greatly increased, and as these measures resulted in very spartan crew compartments the ships' endurance was limited compared with Allied escorts.

2 The form of the bridge was also altered to allow rapid building. The cross-section was hexagonal, and there were no more rounded shapes.

3 The lookout post, or crow's nest, on the topmast of the forward tripod mast, was omitted.

4 The tripod mainmast was arranged in such as way that a 25mm triple could be installed on the deck superstructure behind it.

5 The superstructure was lengthened.

6 The funnel was no longer round or oval, but hexagonal.

7 The three 120mm AA guns (1 twin, 1 single mount) were arranged as on the *Mikura* class in 'A' and 'Y' positions. The difference was just that the ships of the earlier phase, which were laid down up to about June 1944, had the same protective shield as the *Mikura* class on the forward mounting, while the others had a modified version of new shape.

8 The ships were fitted with five 25mm triple gun mounts, which were installed as on the *Mikura* class after the alteration in armament. The AA bandstands at the bridge position and abreast the funnel were no longer supported by three narrow stanchions, but by a single, broad, pierced support. The single AA gun in front of the bridge, and the 80mm trench mortar were also built in at the same time. Some of the ships were later fitted with a further four 25mm machine guns in single mounts, which were set up on the forecastle.

9 The nine ships built by the Hitachi shipbuilding company, based in Sakurajima, and which have already been mentioned in connection with the *Mikura* class[11], were fitted with three Model 94 depth-charge throwers, three Model 3 loading frames, two depth-charge rails, one pair of large minesweeping devices, and one pair of paravanes.

On the remaining ships this equipment was omitted entirely, and they were fitted instead with 16 Model 3 depth charge throwers (1943)[12].

After completion most ships had the minesweeping equipment removed.

10 From the outset the foremast platform was designed to take the aerial for the Type 22 radar unit, while the aerial for the Type 13 was installed either to the front, to the side, or to the rear of the mainmast after completion.

11 The underwater locating equipment consisted of a sound navigation and ranging unit (Sonar) Type 93 – on later ships this was changed for two Type 3 Model 2 Sonar units – and an underwater listening unit (hydrophone) Type 93.

12 The number of generators was reduced from 3 to 2.

This simplified design was applied to the Type A vessels approved in the Urgent War Programme of 1941, but only to those ships which had not yet been started. This double alteration in the design plans explains the confusion in the building numbers in the Programme mentioned above concerning the ships of the *Etorofu*, *Mikura* and *Ukuru* classes. In total 29 ships of the improved Type B ships were built together with those approved in later programmes. Four were uncompleted at the end of the war, and 20 were cancelled.

On average four months were required to build each ship. The hull form, greatly simplified compared with conventional shapes, and the use of sectional building methods, reduced the required man-days to 42,000.

TABLE 6: CLASS TECHNICAL DETAILS

	Etorofu	*Mikura*	*Ukuru*
Basic Planning number	E 19	E 20	E 20 B
Building number	310	320	332
Standard displacement	870 tons		940 tons
Trial displacement		1020 tons	
Length between perpendiculars		75.2m/237ft 11in	
Waterline length	76.2m/250ft	77.5m/254ft 4in	76.5m/251ft
Overall length	77.7m/255ft		78.7m/258ft 5in
Waterline beam		9.1m/29ft 10in	
Side height		5.3m/17ft 5in	5.34m/17ft 5in
Average draught	3.05m/10ft		
Machinery	2 No 22 type 10 diesels ((4200bhp)	as *Etorofu*	
Speed	19.7kts		19.5kts
No of propellers and rpm	2 × 510rpm		2 × 510rpm
Fuel	207 tons		120 tons
Range	8000nm/16kts		5000nm/16kts
Armament	3 × 12cm	3 × 12cm (1×2, 1×1)	as *Mikura* except
	4 × 25mm (2×2)	4 × 25mm (2×2)	6 × 25mm (2×2)
	36 Mod 95 depth charges	120 Mod 95 depth charges	
	Mod 94 thrower	2 Mod 94 throwers	
	Mod 3 loading frame	2 Mod 3 loading frame	16 Mod 3 loading frame
Additional armament	as *Shimushu* class	10 × 25mm	
		8cm army mortar	
Sensors	radar as *Shimushu* class plus Mod E 27 radar intercept receiver (all classes) on tripod mast behind bridge		
	Mod 93 sonar	Mod 93 sonar (2 Type	
	Mod 93 hydrophone	2 after April 1944 all classes) Mod 93 hydrophone	
Crew (according to budget)	147	150	

TABLE 7: CLASS OUTLINES

5	310	*Etorofu*	Hitachi, Sakurajima	23.2.42	29.1.43	15.5.43
6	311	*Matsuwa*	Mitsui, Tamano	20.4.42	13.11.42	23.3.43
7	312	*Sado*	Tsurumi	21.2.42	28.11.42	27.3.43
8	313	*Oki*	Uraga Dock	27.2.42	20.10.42	28.3.43
9	314	*Mutsura*	Hitachi, Sakurajima	25.7.42	10.4.43	31.7.43
10	315	*Iki*	Mitsui, Tamano	2.5.42	5.2.43	31.5.43
11	316	*Tsushima*	Tsurumi	20.6.42	20.3.43	28.7.43
12	317	*Wakamiya*	Mitsui, Tamano	16.7.42	19.4.43	10.8.43
13	318	*Hirado*	Hitachi, Sakurajima	2.11.42	30.6.43	28.9.43
14	319	*Fukue*	Uraga Dock	30.10.43	2.4.43	28.6.43
15	321	*Amakusa*	Hitachi, Sakurajima	5.4.43	31.9.43	20.11.43
16	323	*Monju*	Mitsui, Tamano	15.2.43	31.7.43	30.11.43
17	325	*Kanju*	Uraga Dock	8.4.43	7.8.43	30.10.43
18	330	*Kasado*	Uraga Dock	10.8.43	9.12.43	27.2.44
19	320	*Mikura*	Tsurumi	1.10.42	16.7.43	31.10.43
20	322	*Miyake*	Tsurumi	22.2.43	30.8.43	30.11.43
21	329	*Awaji*	Hitachi, Sakurajima	1.6.43	30.10.43	25.1.44
22	326	*Nami*	Hitachi, Sakurajima	10.8.43	3.12.43	28.2.44
23	327	*Kurahashi*	Tsurumi	1.6.43	15.10.43	19.2.44
24	328	*Yashiro*	Hitachi, Sakurajima	18.11.43	16.2.44	10.5.44
25	329	*Chiburi*	Tsurumi	20.7.43	30.11.43	3.4.44
26	334	*Kusagaki*	Tsurumi	7.9.43	22.1.44	31.5.44
27	331	*Hiburi*	Hitachi, Sakurajima	3.1.44	10.4.44	27.6.44
28	332	*Ukuru*	Tsurumi	9.10.43	15.5.44	31.7.44
29	333	*Daito*	Hitachi, Sakurajima	17.4.44	24.6.44	7.8.44
30	335	*Okinawa*	Tsurumi	10.12.43	19.6.44	16.8.44
31	336	*Amami*	Tsurumi	14.2.44	13.11.44	8.4.45
32	337	*Aguni*	Tsurumi	5.2.44	21.9.44	2.12.44
33	338	*Shinnan*	Uraga Dock	24.5.44	5.9.44	21.10.44
37	339	*Shonan*	Hitachi, Sakurajima	23.2.44	19.5.44	13.7.44
35	5251	*Yaku*	Uraga Dock	24.5.44	5.9.44	23.10.44
36	5252	*Kume*	Hitachi, Sakurajima	26.5.44	15.8.44	25.9.44
37	5253	*Chikubu*	Uraga Dock	8.9.44	24.11.44	31.12.44
38	5254	*Ikuna*	Hitachi, Sakurajima	30.6.44	4.9.44	15.10.44
39	5255	*Kozu*	Uraga Dock	20.10.44	31.12.44	7.2.45
40	5256	*Hotaka*	Uraga Dock	27.11.44	28.1.45	30.3.45
41	5257	*Shisaka*	Hitachi, Sakurajima	21.8.44	31.10.44	15.12.44
42	5258	*Ikara*	Uraga Dock	26.12.44	22.2.45	30.4.45
43	5259	*Sakito*	Hitachi, Sakurajima	7.9.44	29.11.44	10.1.45
44	5260	*Ikino*	Uraga Dock	3.1.45	11.3.45	17.7.45
45	5262	*Mokuto*	Hitachi, Sakurajima	5.11.44	7.1.45	19.2.45
46	5264	*Habuto*	Hitachi, Sakurajima	3.12.44	28.2.45	7.4.45
47	4701	*Inagi*	Mitsui, Tamano	15.5.44	25.5.44	16.12.44
48	4702	*Habushi*	Mitsui, Tamano	20.8.44	20.11.44	10.1.45
49	4703	*Ojika* ex *Oga*	Mitsui, Tamano	7.9.44	30.12.44	21.2.45
50	4704	*Kanawa*	Mitsui, Tamano	15.11.44	20.1.45	15.3.45
51	4705	*Uku*	Marinearsenal, Sasebo	1.8.44	19.11.44	25.1.45
52	4707	*Takane*	Mitsui, Tamano	15.12.44	13.2.45	26.4.45
53	4709	*Kuga*	Marinearsenal, Sasebo	1.8.44	19.11.44	25.1.45
54	4711	*Shiga*	Marinearsenal, Sasebo	25.11.44	9.2.45	20.3.45
55	4712	*Io*	Marinearsenal, Sasebo	25.11.44	12.2.45	24.3.45

Note: Fates follow on p180.

However, efforts continued to reduce this time to 30,000 once the yards had gained some experience.

The desired number of ships was not achieved. The reasons were as follows: First, the emphasis was switched to Types C and D; and second, there were problems with the main engines, since diesels simply could not be built fast enough.

Towards the end of the war this type was used as a command ship for Type C and D vessels.

During the war seven ships were sunk. The remainder were used almost exclusively for minesweeping and repatriation duties, and thereafter were distributed among the Allies as spoils of war. Five ships were passed to the hydrographic office as weather stations and survey ships; later they were also used for patrol duties and remained on the effective list until 1966. One ship, the *Kojima* (ex-CD *Shiga*), was given to the town of Chiba, where she still serves the population of the Inage area.

NOTES

7 The power of the diesel engines on the *Shimushu* class was raised to 4500bhp (3310kW) by raising the revolutions. On the *Etorofu* class the same diesels (Model 10 Nr 22) produced 4200bhp (3089kW) at 510rpm. The top speed remained the same, nevertheless.

8 Hydrophones are passive locating devices, ie listening systems, which register sounds which are detected in the water (shaft, propeller, engine noises, etc). They can be used to indicate the direction only, and not the range. The Model 93 (1933)

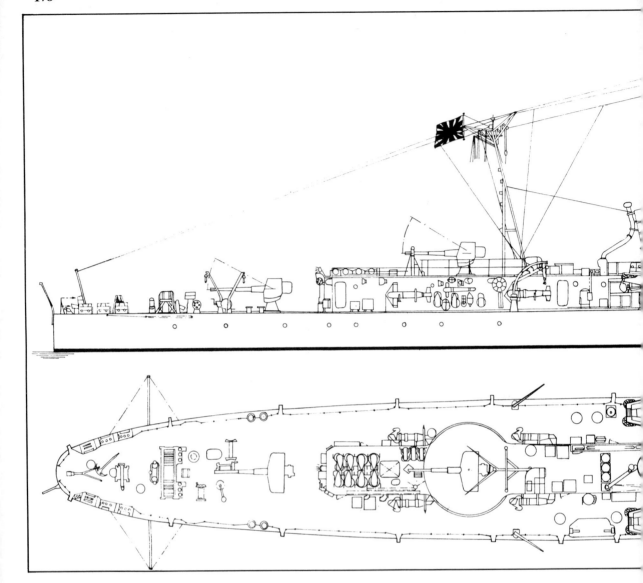

Sketch 3 Type A, *Etorofu* class: *Iki* after completion (June 1943). Very similar to the *Shimushu* class when completed, but with command bridge extended farther forward, different bow shape, some ships with tapered funnel etc.

hydrophone had 15 microphones, which were attached close to the bow in the form of an ellipse. If the speed of the submerged submarine was 3kts, the system's performance was as shown in the table:

Own speed (kts)	Kagero	Hatsutsuki	Shimakaze	Arashi
0				5500 (5)
6		5000 (3)		
8	3200 (1)			
12	1400 (3)	2600 (3)	6000 (3)	4000 (5)
14	1000 (1)	2000 (3)		
18				3000 (5)
20				2000 (5)
22			4000	

Note: All distance figures in m. Figures in brackets indicate the variation in direction in degrees.

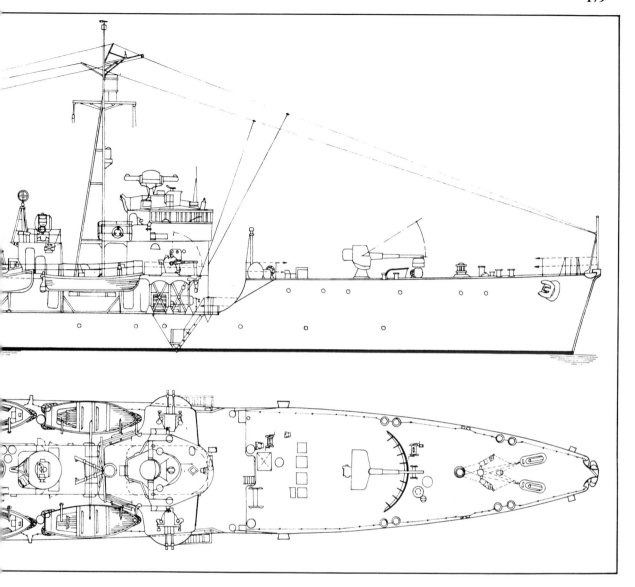

9 Although the standard displacement rose by 70 tons to 940 tons, the increase was almost entirely the result of increased equipment and alterations to the armament.

10 The performance of the Model 3 Type 2 Sonar *(3 Shiki 2 gata suichi tanshingi)* was, in the example of *Hiburi*, (a ship of the *Ukuru* class), as follows (pertaining to a submarine travelling submerged at 3 knots):

Own speed (kts)	Range (m)	Submarine's depth
10	3500	30
	3000	60
14	2500	30
	1200	60
16	1000	

11 In this text only *Mikura, Miyake, Awaji, Nomi, Kurahashi, Yashiro, Chiburi Kusagaki* are included as *Mikura* class. Officially, however, the ships *Hiburi, Daito, Shonan* (urgent war

programme), *Kume, Ikuna, Shisaka, Sakito, Mokuto, Habuto* (modified fifth programme), built by the Hitachi shipbuilding AG at the Sakurajima yard, and also the ships *Otsu* and *Tomoshiri,* which were not finished at the end of the war, were also classed as *Mikura* class. The reason for this lies exclusively in their minesweeping devices, and the use of depth-charge throwers and loading frames of the *Mikura* class. As far as the hull was concerned, they were identical to the *Ukuru* class, and hence it seems more appropriate to class them as such.

12 The Model 3 depth-charge launcher was a device intended especially for coast defence ships. The special feature was that half of the firing tube lay below the upper deck, which considerably simplified the loading process. The installation was admittedly rather complex. The total weight was 370kg, the firing tube was inclined outwards at an angle of 50°. The performance was the same as that of the Model 94. The depth-charges were brought from the storage compartments onto the loading ramp with a dredging lift; the slow rate of hoisting using the manually-operated davits was thereby eliminated. In front of the loading ramp they could either be thrown over the rollers

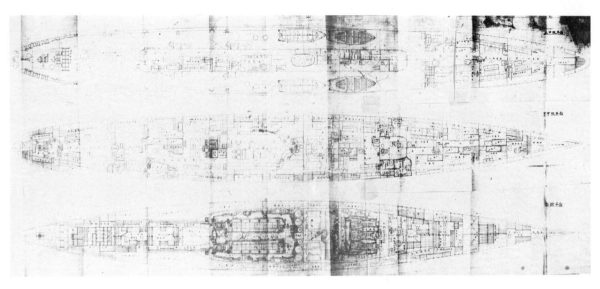

The upper, middle and hold decks of the *Etorofu* class.
Author's collection

onto the depth-charge thrower, or over the run-off frames over the stern.

This was a well thought-out and effective system; the efficiency of the British Hedgehog thrower was not yet achieved, however. The method of working, the installation and the arrangement of the throwers is shown in sketch 6.

Sketch 4 Type A, *Mikura* class: *Yashiro* after alteration of the light AA weapons and fitting of Type 13 and Type 22 radars.

FATES
5 Repatriation. To USA, 5.8.47 BU at Harima, Kure.
6 Sunk 22.8.44 US submarine *Harder* 14° 15′N/120° 05″0 23 miles W of Manila.
7 Sunk 22.8.44 US submarine *Haddo* as *Matsuwa*.
8 Repatriation. Tsingtao 29.8.47 to China as *Chang Pei*.

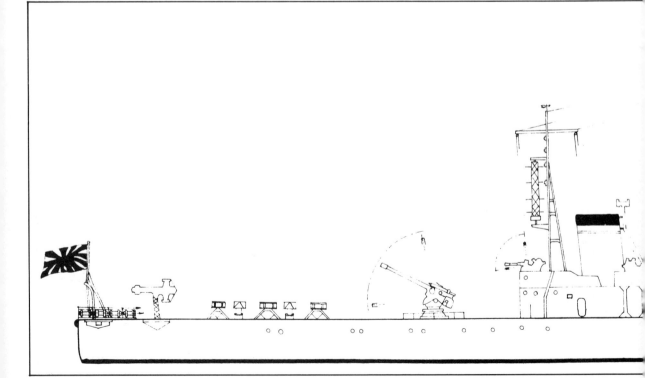

9 Sunk 2.9.43 US submarine *Snapper* (08° 40′N/151° 31′0, 85 miles NNW Truk Island).

10 Sunk 24.5.44 US submarine *Raton* (01° 26′N/149° 20′0, South China Sea – Dutch-East Indies area).

11 Repatriation. Shanghai 31.7.47 to China as *Lin An*.

12 Sunk 23.11.43 US submarine *Gudgeon* (28° 49′N/122° 11′0 Eastward of China Sea, 70 miles S of Shushan island).

13 Sunk 12.9.44 US submarine *Growler* (17° 54′N/114° 49′0, South China Sea – 250 miles E of Hainan Island).

14 Moderate damage 1.3.45 from US aircraft. Repatriation, 16.7.47 Singapore to England.

15 Sunk 9.8.45 US and British carrier aircraft (38° 26′N/141° 30′0, Bay of Onogawa, near Miyazaki, N of Honshu).

16 Severely damaged 3.4.45 by US aircraft in Hongkong. BU Japan.

17 Sunk 15.9.45 Russian aircraft off Ubrisan (North Korea).

18 Bow separated 22.6.45 by torpedo from US submarine *Crevalle*; emergency repair in Ominato, 20.8.45 to Sasebo, BU there.

19 Sunk 28.3.45 US submarine *Threadfin* (31° 49′N/131° 44′0 near Kyushu).

20 Planned for repatriation, struck mine 21.8.45 at Moji, out of action, not repaired, BU in Sasebo.

21 Sunk 2.6.44 US submarine *Guitarro* (220° 34′N/121° 51′0 between Formosa and Yosho Island).

22 Sunk 14.4.45 US submarine *Tirante* (35° 25′N/126° 15′0 West of Quelpart island – East China Sea).

23 Minesweeping, to England 14.9.47, bought back and BU in Nagoya.

24 Minesweeping. Tsingtao 29.8.47 to China as *Cheng An*.

25 Sunk 12.1.45 US carrier aircraft (10° 20′N/107° 50′0 South China Sea)

26 Sunk 7.8.44 US submarine *Guitarro* (14° 51′N/119° 59′0, 60 miles W of Manila).

27 Sunk 22.8.44 US submarine *Harder* (14° 15′N/120° 05′0, 35 miles WSW of Manila).

28 Minesweeping until 1947. *Ukuru Maru*, 1947 observation ship MSF. *Satsuma* 1954 (PL 109) JMSDF.

29 Minesweeping, sunk 16.11.45 after striking mine in the straits of Tsushima

30 Sunk 30.7.45 US carrier aircraft (35° 30′N/135° 21′0 NNW Maizuru).

31 Repatriation, to England 10.9.47, bought back and BU at Hiroshima.

32 Severely damaged 27.5.45 (bow removed) not repaired, BU.

33 Minesweeping until 1947. Became *Shinnan Maru* MFS. Became *Tsugaru* (PL 105) JMSDF 1954.

34 Sunk 26.2.45 US submarine *Hoe* (17° 08′N/110° 01′0, S of Hainan Island).

35 Sunk 23.2.45 US submarine *Hammerhead* (12° 30′N/109° 29′0, off Indochina).

36 Sunk 28.1.45 US submarine *Spadefish* (33° 56′N/123° 06′0, Yellow Sea).

37 Minesweeping until 1947. Became *Chikubu Maru* 1947. Became *Atsumi* (PL 103) JMSDF 1954.

38 Minesweeping until 1947. Became *Ikuna Maru*. (Observation ship weather station, transport ministry). Became *Ojika* (PL 102) JMSDF 1954.

39 Minesweeping. To USSR 28.7.45 at Nakhodka.

40 Repatriation, to USA 19.7.47, bought back and BU Uraga.

41 Repatriation. Shanghai 6.7.47 to China as *Hui An*.

42 Minesweeping, damaged in Kaguchi Passage 1.8.45. Sunk after end of the war, raised and BU.

43 Minesweeping, moderate damage 27.6.45 in Chokyo Passage off Nagoshia (S Korea). BU Sasebo.

44 Repatriation. To USSR 29.7.47 at Nakhodka.

45 Sunk 4.4.45 by mine in Shimonoseki straits, 4 miles off Buzaki Lighthouse.

46 Repatriation. Singapore 16.7.47 to England.

47 Sunk 9.8.45 US carrier aircraft (38° 26′N/141° 30′, off bay of Onagona N of Honshu).

48 Repatriation. To USA at Kure 6.9.47 bought back BU Kure.

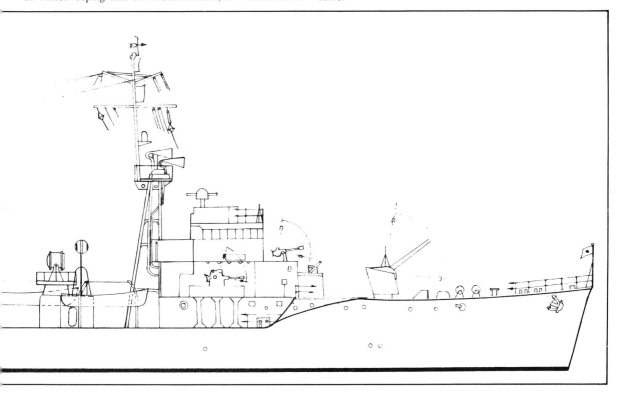

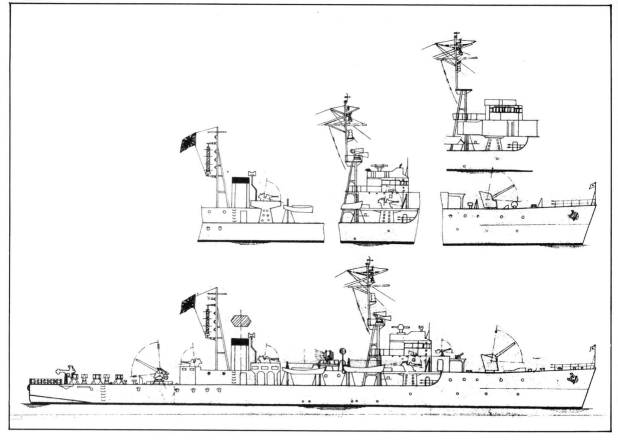

Sketch 5 Type A, *Ukuru* class: *Shonan* with depth-charge throwers and *Mikura* class minesweeping devices after reinforcement of the light AA weapons.

Small sketch, right bottom and centre: *Shisaka;* compare shape of the bridge and the protective shield.

Small sketch, left: Shape of the 25mm machine gun platform on the *Amami* and other ships.

Small sketch, top right: Appearance of *Kanawa* before delivery to the Royal Navy.

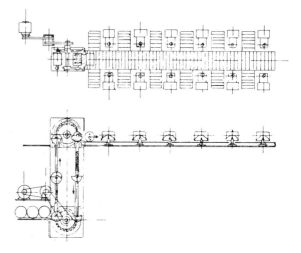

Sketch 6 Details of the depth charge system (in this case 12 throwers), and especially the supply line from the storage compartments aft.

49 Sunk 2.5.45 US submarine *Springer* (33° 58′N/122° 58′0, Yellow Sea)
50 Repatriation. Singapore 14.8.47 to England.
51 Slightly damaged by US carrier aircraft 28.4.45. Slightly damaged 9.5.45 by mine W of Straits of Shimanoski. Repatriation, to USA at Tsingtao 4.7.47.

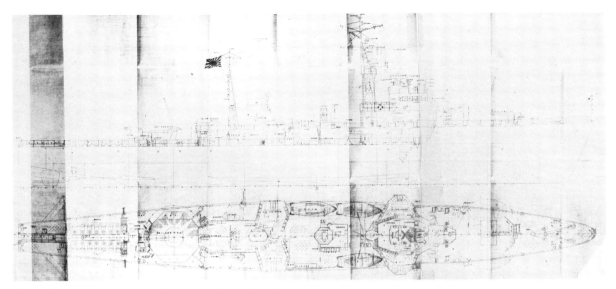

Elevation and upper deck 1:50 plans of the *Ukuru* class *Uku*.
Author's collection

The Type B *Ukuru* class *Amami* on her trials off Yokohama in
April 1945. She has Type 22 radar on the mainmast.
Author's collection

52 Damaged by bomb hit close to Maizuru from carrier aircraft
30.7.45. BU Kure.
53 Struck by mine in Fukugowa gulf 25.6.45. Not repaired, BU
Maizuru.
54 Minesweeping. Became *Shiga Maru* 1947, MSF 1948.
Koyima (PL 106) in JMSDF in 1955.
55 Repatriation, hotel ship in Senzaki from 4.46. BU Sasebo.

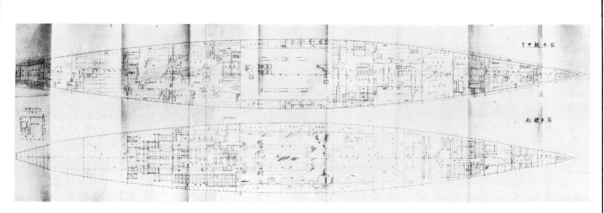

Middle and hold decks of the *Ukuru* class *Uku*.
Author's collection

The Type B *Mikura* class *Awaji* off Awajishima (Osaka Bay)
after her completion in January 1944.
Author's collection

The Gunboat Tyr

By Frank Abelsen

When England, France and USA began to build ironc-lads between 1850 and 1860 wooden warships rapidly became obsolete. The Royal Norwegian Navy therefore went into its gunboat period. The Navy Commission fleet plan of 1855 envisaged building 12 steam-gunboats. It was later intended to build the gunboats in three classes.

In the Navy's new fleet plan of 1877 we find 12 first class gunboats, 24 second class gunboats and 46 third class gunboats.

But the Navy's budget for the new construction was reduced during the following years, and the value of the existing warships was reduced by technological developments.

The decay of the Navy was a fact. Some of it could be attributed to the Navy Department and the Army Department being united into the Defence Department

in 1884. The Army was much bigger than the Navy and considered to be the main force. Consequently, an Army officer headed the Defence Department.

At this time it was also said that the Navy's main task was to enfilade the land approach to Kristiania, the capital of Norway, from the fjord within Oscarsborg, the coastal defence fortification in Oslo-fjord. The Navy was forced by financial economies into sheltered waters as a defensive coastal defence force.

The first class gunboats had to be constructed with very good sea-going qualities for duty along Norway's northern coast. Only four were built and they were all of different design. The third class gunboats were, for economy's sake, converted from 18 old row gun-barges.

In the years from 1874 to 1887 seven second class gunboats were built at the Carljohansvern Shipyard in Horten, the main naval base in Norway. They were *Vale, Uller, Nor, Brage, Vidar, Gor* and *Tyr*.

This class was modelled after the British gunboat

General arrangement (1:50) of the gunboat *Tyr* 1946.

The Naval Museum, Norway

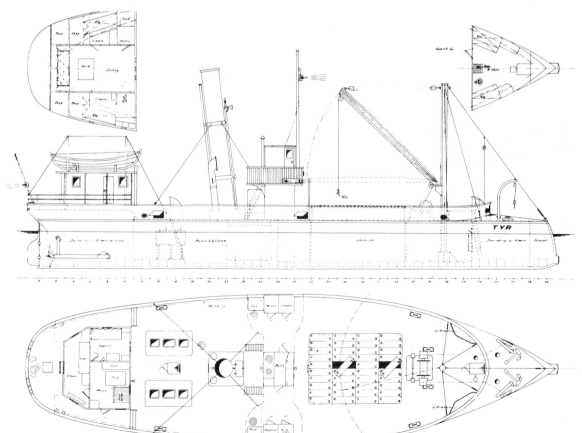

Pl. XXXIX

General arrangement of the second class gunboat *Gor*.

The Naval Museum, Norway

HMS *Staunch*. Advocates of the 'skerries-tactic' saw this type of gunboat to be 'nearly' ideal. They should lie behind islets and skerries (reefs), waiting in ambush with their heavy guns. *Gor* and *Tyr* were the first warships built of steel in Norway. The remaining ships were built of iron.

All their names came from the Scandinavian mythology. *Tyr* was the son of Odin, and he was the proper god of war. He ruled over victory in battle. The day of the week, Tuesday, in Norwegian 'Tirsdag', comes from *Tyr*, and there are many place names in Norway derived from him.

CHARACTERISTICS

The gunboat *Tyr* was launched on 16 March 1887 at the Carljohansvern Shipyard in Horten. Her total cost was 356,557,00 Norwegian crowns. *Tyr* had a displacement of 294 tons, and her dimensions were, length (oa) 31.8m (104ft 4in), beam 8.5m (27ft 11in) and draught 2.2m (7ft 3in). Her machinery consisted of two vertical compound steam engines and two cylinder tube boilers with a pressure of 6.5kg/cm². This gave 450ihp and a maximum speed of 10.5 knots. The bunkers held 22 tons of coal and she had an action radius of 750 miles at 8 knots. The complement was 44 men. This class was originally armed with one 27cm (10.6in) L/13 muzzle loading gun from Armstrong, as the main armament.

Gor and *Tyr* were on the other hand armed with one 26cm (10.5in) L/30 breech loading gun from Krupp as the main armament. This gun weighed 25.2 tons and the mountings about 14 tons. The heavy armament claimed nearly 14 per cent of the largest displacement which was disproportionately large. Their whole firepower lay in this sole gun. The gunboat could not catch any enemy, but had to wait until a vessel came within range. Then the gunboat could be very dangerous.

The big gun could fire a steel- or cast iron shell of 275kg (606lb) with a charge of 87kg (191lb) prismatic brown powder, and the muzzle velocity was 520m/sec. With the explosive composition of 10.5kg (23lb) the steel shell could at quite close range, penetrate wrought iron plating of 52cm (20.4in). The range was 4000m at 5° elevation, and the gun crew numbered 13 men. They needed 6 minutes to fire a round. The gun was mounted on a slide-mounting which was fixed to the deck. So traversing meant moving the ship. Between the mounting and the gun-carriage there was a hydraulic break, filled with a mixture of glycerine and water. The advance of the gun-carriage had to be done with a tackle.

Tyr had as secondary armament, one Hotchkiss 57mm quick-firing gun, which is now exhibited at the Norwegian Naval Museum in Horten, and two Hotchkiss 37mm revolver-guns. In addition *Gor* and *Tyr* had one 356mm (14in) underwater torpedo tube for Whitehead torpedoes, mounted in the bow.

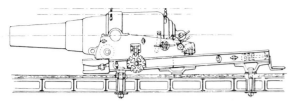

Armstrong 270mm (10.6in) L/13 muzzle loading gun, original main armament of Norwegian second class gunboats.

Drawing from The Norwegian Sea Defences 1814–1914

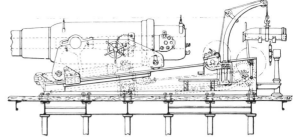

Krupp 260mm (10.2in) L/30 breech loading gun, *Tyr*'s main armament.

Drawing from The Norwegian Sea Defences 1814–1914

SERVICE CAREER

Tyr took part in the yearly division cruise and torpedo exercises. She also joined the mobilisation exercise in September 1895. But in 1900 the gunboat was laid up until the mobilisation in 1905. *Tyr* was then stationed with the Hvaler division.

By this time the gunboat-age of the Navy was ending. This type of ship was out of date. From 14 April 1910 *Tyr* served as a tender to the first Norwegian submarine *Kobben*. This duty went on until 31 December 1913.

Tyr, as well as gunboats of the third class, were afterwards converted into minelayers intended for laying

Armstrong 267mm (10.5in) L/19 no 3 gun aboard the gunboat *Brage* 1905.

The Naval Museum, Norway

temporary mine-barriers in closed waters. *Tyr* was equipped with mine-tracks to take 55 contact mines. Their heavy guns were taken on shore and replaced with a Belgian 120mm quick-firing Cockerfill gun. The secondary armament was replaced with one 76mm quick-firing gun, probably a Bofors L/50, and two 37mm quick-firing guns, probably Hotchkiss.

At the outbreak of World War I *Tyr* was again stationed in the Hvaler-division, as a minelayer in defence of Norwegian neutrality. The division had its base at the Hvaler islands, farthest out in the Oslofjord. The unit's role was to disarm and demolish drifing mines, and to pick up dead bodies. During the war 222

188

dead bodies were picked up around the Norwegian coast. The defence of neutrality was rounded off from 13 November 1918 to 1 April 1919 with guard duty and the seeking of drifting mines. After this was *Tyr* was laid up as too old for naval duty.

In the autumn of 1939 at the outbreak of World War II, *Tyr* and her sister ships were again fitted out for the defence of neutrality. The Royal Norwegian Navy consisted of essentially the same ships as in 1914, except for 19 ships built since 1918 of which only five were of modern design. On 8 April 1940 the Navy consisted of 111 ships. Of these there were 62 real warships, but 43 of them had been built between 1874 and 1918. The remainder were 49 hired whalers, trawlers and coastal passenger steamers, used for guard duties.

WORLD WAR II

Tyr was assigned to the Bergen Squadron with the Second Minelayer Division. Her captain, F Ulstrup, also commanded the division. The gunboat/minelayer was stationed at the small seaport of Klokkarvik in the Lerøy guard section.

In the night of 8/9 April, at about 0030, Captain Ulstrup was informed that the Rauøy and Bolærne forts in the outer Oslofjord were engaging unknown warships. Captain Ulstrup immediately gave orders to clear the ship for action and to get the mines ready for laying. When the first German warships from Group 3, the Bergen Group entered the Korsfjord, *Tyr* went out to lay the mines in the strait between Sotra island and Lerøy. Without being observed by the German force, *Tyr* managed to lay seven mines before the warships were too close for comfort. After that *Tyr* went northward and laid 16 mines at the southern end of Vatlestraumen, a very narrow strait at the southern approach to Bergen. This minelaying also went unobserved by the Germans.

But the German warships (the cruisers *Köln* and *Königsberg*, the gunnery training ships *Bremse*, and depot ship *Carl Peters*, the torpedo boats *Leopard* and *Wolf* and five S-boats) passed the minefields without detonating any of the mines. The return voyage was a different story.

When the cruiser *Köln*, in the evening of 9 April, went out from Bergen to go back to Germany, she put out an Oropessa sweep. Several moored contact mines were cut and the minefield was discovered. But that did not prevent the German transport *Sao Paulo* of 5000grt hitting one of *Tyr*'s mines later that evening. *Sao Paulo* sank immediately with heavy loss of human life and war material.

The Germans had no minesweeper in the area. So the German vessels *Schiff 9*, *Cremon* and launches from *Carl Peters* were ordered to sweep the waters around Vatlestraumen. They sailed from Bergen on the evening of 10 April. *Schiff 9* hit a mine at 19.25 and went down within one or two minutes. *Cremon* hurried to pick up survivors but five minutes later also hit a mine as did one of the launches. The mines from *Tyr* also sank the German 8500grt cargo ship *Liège* on 27 April and in middle of May another cargo ship hit a mine and sank.

Hotchkiss HK 57mm L/44 gun.
The Naval Museum, Norway

The gunboat *Gor*.
The Naval Museum, Norway

After the minelaying *Tyr* carried on with the guard duty in the southern approach to Bergen. She spotted a German S-boat near the island of Skorpo. *Tyr* opened fire and the S-boat replied with her 20mm machine gun. The S-boat manoeuvred clear of the gunfire from *Tyr* which took cover near a small island. *Tyr* carried on southward, but was attacked by three S-boats, one of them being hit by a 37mm shell from *Tyr*. The second S-boat stopped to help the damaged boat while the third S-boat carried on with the shooting. After a while the German S-boats withdrew from the fight and disappeared to the northward.

During the evening of 16 April *Tyr* withdrew into Uskedal, a small seaport on the outer Hardangerfjord. Captain Ulstrup was now commander of the newly established Hardangerfjord Sea Defence Section. The command of *Tyr* was taken over by the second officer, Sub-lieutenant K Sandnæs.

During the battle at Uskedal in the night of the 19-20 April *Tyr* managed with her 120mm gun to damage the German *Schiff 18* so seriously that the ship was run aground. From her were landed German troops, north of Uskedal, and *Tyr* was then in the middle of Storsund just out of Uskedal and fired upon the German positions ashore. The German soldiers fired back with their heavy machine guns and at the same time the gunnery training ship *Bremse* opened fire from the western entrance of Uskedal. The situation was now so dangerous that *Tyr* withdrew from the engagement and went back to the port. *Tyr* received orders to go out again to assist the Norwegian torpedo boat *Stegg* which was engaging *Bremse*.

As soon as *Tyr* showed up in the strait *Bremse* started firing at her again. *Tyr* therefore steamed across the strait and into a bay where she took cover. Sub-lieutenant Sandnæs saw that further fighting was hopeless and received orders to prepare to destroy the ship. The crew went ashore to get some rest. When they tried to move weapons and ammunition ashore, two German S-boats came into the Storsund at high speed and came alongside *Tyr*. The Norwegian crew hid on the island while the Germans took over *Tyr*. A German trawler came and took *Tyr* under tow back to Uskedal.

IN GERMAN HANDS

The German force left the area at Uskedal in the morning of 20 April after the Norwegian force had retreated. *Tyr* was sailed to Bergen under German flag and with a German crew. The German Admiral Schrader decided on 30 April to lay a minebarrier in the entrance of Sognefjord to catch the Norwegian warships, which still operated in the fjord. The minelayers *Try* and *Uller*, also captured by the Germans, were to be used for the tak. The ships had about 80 mines on board and were commanded by *Korvetten-Kapitän* Borchardt.

Norwegian intelligence in this area was very effective and the two minelayers were observed throughout their advance. Two Norwegian aircraft, F-312 and F-334, took off and attacked *Tyr* and *Uller*. They dropped nine bombs without hitting either ship, but three Germans aboard *Uller* were wounded by a splinter. After the attack *Tyr* and *Uller* continued towards the Sognefjord where they began to lay the mines. In the night another Norwegian aircraft, F-58, made two dive bomber attacks. One 250kg bomb and four 50g bombs were dropped, but there was no direct hit. One bomb exploded close to *Uller* which was so damaged that she took in water. *Uller* was therefore grounded at the southern end of Losneøy. *Tyr* only received minor damage. The aircraft was exposed to heavy gunfire from the minelayers without being hit and it returned to the base.

The minelaying stopped and the crew of *Uller* were taken onboard *Tyr*. Thereafter *Uller* was fired on until she began to burn. Early in the morning *Tyr* sailed southward towards Bergen. But once again she was followed by coast watchers. When *Tyr* steered down the Fålefotsund, a very narrow strait between Hissøy island and the mainland, the crew from a Norwegian guardboat were waiting for her and opened fire with machine guns from both sides of the strait. How many of the estimated 36 German soldiers were killed or wounded is not known. The Germans replied with the 120mm gun and small arms without hitting any of the Norwegians. The shooting stopped when *Tyr* was out of range and the ship continued towards Bergen.

Details of *Tyr*'s subsequent war service under German command are not extant. She was perhaps laid up, because the Germans were of the opinion that the minelayers were hopelessly old. But some of *Tyr*'s sister ships were used by the Germans. *Gor* and *Vale* were used as 'kondensatorschiff' for delivering distillated water. *Vale* was also for a while used as a tug-boat under the 'Hafenkapitän-Bergen'. *Vidar* was captured by the

The car ferry M/S *Bjøorn West*, ex-gunboat *Tyr*.
Photographed by Lars-Helge Isdahl

Germans at Melsomvik on 14 April 1940, entered the *'Hafenschutzflotille Kristiansand-süd'* as *NK-31* and was used as a minelayer. *Nor* was also laid up during the war.

POST-1945 CAREER

After the German capitulation in 1945 the old minelayers were returned to the Royal Norwegian Navy. They were immediately discarded, but *Gor* was used as a water barge until she was condemned and was later broken up. *Nor* was sold in 1949 and was renamed *Flatholm*. She exists today as a lighter.

Tyr was sold in 1946 to the P/R Tyr in Bergen and was rebuilt into a heavy lifting crane ship at the Gravdal Shipyard in Sunde. In 1949 she was sold again, and this time to Brødrene Wilhelmsen A/S in Åsane and completely rebuilt into a car ferry. Renamed as M/F *Bjørn-West* she started her new duty as a car ferry between Knarvik and Steinestø) north of Bergen. The old steam engine was replaced with a 375bhp Deutz diesel motor. This motor was again changed with a 400bhp Wickmann diesel in 1970.

Bjøorn-West was named after the famous Norwegian Milorg Company that operated in the Matre mountains in the winter of 1945. The ferry was taken over by *'A/S Bergen — Nordhordland Trafikklag'* in 1971. This company changed its name to 'Bergen-Nordhordland Rutelag' in 1974. In August 1980 *Bjørn-West* was bought by the A/S Saki (Fredrik Odfjell) Company at a cost of 275,000 Norwegian crowns.

The ship is now used as a supplementary ferry, when other ferry owners need extra help during the summer season. The ferry has also been used to carry heavy rolling-stock to the head of a fjord in Western Norway. It is to be hoped that this ship, which has served her country for nearly a century, will continue to sail for many years to come.

REFERENCES
Den Norske Marine 1865-1950 Særtrykk av Norge på havet.
Det Norske Veritas, skipsliste 1947-1980.
Mineleggerne Gor og Tyre, Rolf Scheen Norges forsvar nr. 10-1960 (artikkel).
Norges Sjøforsvar 1814-1914, Kristiania 1918
Norges Sjøkrig 1939-1940, Rolf Scheen (bind 1-2).
Norges Sjøkrig 1940-1945, bind I, bind III E A Steen, Oslo 1956.
Norges Skipsliste 1947-1980, Sjøfartsdirektoratet.
Sjømilitæret Samfunds Marinekalender 1814-1934 Oslo 1934.
Skipet, organ for Norsk Skipsfartshistorisk selskap Nr. 4 1980.
Skipsbygging på Horten gjennom 150 år Marinens Hovedverft 1968.
Gors og Tyrs artillerimateriell (prlt. G Mørch).
Norsk Tidsskrift for Søvæsen, 5. årgang 1886-1887 Horten 1887.
Haandbog i Søartilleri Horten 1894.
Egne notater.

The Reborn Battleships

by Norman Friedman

The battleship *New Jersey* off the Lebanon on 25 September
1983. She fired 312 16in shells in all.

UPI/Popperfoto

For a quarter century the United States Navy was unique
in the world in having retained four battleships in
reserve. One of them, *New Jersey*, has now been back in
service for over 18 months. *Iowa* should be recommissioned before this article is in print, and the Navy is
seeking funds to recommission the other two ships.
From the Navy's point of view, these ships are an expression of uniquely American naval priorities. They are also
a considerable bargain, since the cost of modernisation
appears to have been less than the price of a new frigate.
The Navy has, however, had to contend with repeated
charges that the battleships are being brought back into
service, not for some vital military role, but out of a
misguided nostalgia. After all, they are unique in the
world, and they are 40 years old.

The recommissioned battleships should fill two complementary primary roles. First, they restore a level of
fire support that the Marines have sorely missed. The
United States now possesses only six ships carrying guns
with calibres greater than 5in: four battleships and two

New Jersey off the Lebanon on 25 September 1983.
UPI/Popperfoto

heavy cruisers (with a third, the much-used *Newport News*, probably good only for cannibalisation). For many years the Marines have noted nervously that the 5in gun of a destroyer actually has a smaller calibre than a standard Soviet weapon, the 130mm (5.1in). This disparity was actually used to justify the development of the ill-fated US 8in lightweight gun. For some years in the 1960s US shipbuilding plans included a specialised Amphibious Fire Support ship (LFS) armed with the new gun and assault rockets, but it never materialised, and Marine Corps amphibious forces actually declined in carrying capacity after Vietnam.

Some even imagined that the United States would never again have to land troops on hostile shores. However, post-Vietnam experience suggested otherwise. Moreover, in the decade since Vietnam, it has become increasingly clear that neither the United States *nor* the Soviet Union may be able to control events in the Third World short of local warfare. That is, the rate of crisis may be increasing, although without any threat of escalation into general war. That is exactly the political climate that demands increased shore bombardment capability – as in Lebanon. In this sense the reappearance of the 16in gun at sea is extremely timely.

BATTLESHIPS AND CARRIERS
Second, as a unit in the Surface Action Groups (SAGs), the battleship can help project US seapower into an increasingly turbulent Third World. Although a SAG clearly cannot match a carrier battle group's capability, only one carrier in three can be on station at any one time, allowing for one under refit and one working up or coming home. This figure can be improved temporarily in an emergency, but the US Navy must plan for sustained deployments. The limitations of the carrier force were particularly highlighted by the decision to maintain major naval forces in the Indian Ocean, following the Soviet invasion of Afghanistan in December 1979. At the time, with 12 active carriers, the United States was maintaining two in the Mediterranean and two in the Western Pacific. The Indian Ocean carrier or carriers had to come from those fleets. However, the two deployed fleets (Sixth and Seventh) were already at a

Two gunners mates stand beside a 16in imitation shell aboard *New Jersey* 29 September 1983. The US Navy still has over 21,000 16in shells.
UPI/Popperfoto

bare minimum of strength. Ideally, carriers should always operate in pairs, so that even the current goal of 16 is short of what it would take to form three deployed fleets. SAGs can go part of the way to make up the difference.

Indeed, under some circumstances long-range gunfire

New Jersey fires for the first time since Vietnam 1969 on 14 December 1983. She fired 11 rounds (out of 71 from 3 ships) against Syrian AA positions inland after US reconnaissance jets were fired at. The photograph is an extreme enlargement from a colour slide taken by USMC 1st Lieutenant Bob Dillon from the Marine position at the airport.

UPI/US Marine Corps

may be preferable to carrier air attacks. For example, they do not risk the loss of valuable pilots, as in Lebanon. Some would suggest that it is peculiarly disheartening to the victims of shelling that they cannot hope to do anything about the attack. They can at least shoot back at aircraft. This is hardly to suggest that the gun can somehow be revived in such a way as to supplant aircraft, but only that, within its niche, the gun remains valuable.

It can be argued, too, that the battleships are potentially extremely valuable as fleet flagships, replacing the missile cruisers of the 1960s and 1970s, the last of which,

New Jersey off the Lebanon on 13 January 1984. Two days later she fired on Druze positions with her 16in and 5in guns.

UPI/Popperfoto

Oklahoma City, was retired in 1979. Such a configuration was studied in 1981, but rejected for the time being as too expensive. However, a flagship conversion would be a viable possibility for a future large battleship refit. See the earlier article (Issue 19) on the command cruisers for the continuing significance of flagship capacity at sea. Certainly fast battleships such as the *Iowa*s were valuable as flagships within wartime and postwar fast carrier task forces.

Battleship survivability is an important element of all of these proposals. Anti-ship missiles, such as Exocet, are now the common coin of Third World navies. Although a fleet at sea should be able to deal relatively easily with such weapons, the prospect of surprise attack remains sobering. Carriers have always been vulnerable, in that by they have on board large masses of explosives and highly inflammable jet fuels. A battleship is different. She has only very limited volumes of explosives, primarily well below the waterline. The new missile installations are all above deck, unconnected to magazines or other explosive concentrations below. A small missile would be unlikely, then, to do very much damage. Massive side armour (7in–12in for the *Iowa*s)

would help a battleship resist most current forms of attack. Note that there are so few armoured warships in the world that there are very few armour-piercing weapons. In this sense, the gross obsolescence of the battleship is a major asset. This is not to say that a ship like *New Jersey* cannot be sunk, only that sinking her is no trivial matter.

GUNFIRE SUPPORT
From the Marine's point of view, the 1960s and 1970s were extremely depressing times. They had long believed that naval gunfire was essential to the success of any opposed landing. Although they hoped to achieve a measure of surprise through techniques such as helicopter assault, they were uncomfortably aware of the decline of the heavy (8in and 16in) gun in the active and then in the reserve fleets. There were two attempts to solve this problem: an abortive Landing Fire Support Weapon, which would have been compatible with Terrier missile launchers; and the 8in lightweight gun. The gun was actually built, and mounted aboard the destroyer *Hull*, but it was cancelled due to lack of funds. It was suggested, too, that a single 8in gun, incapable of firing smothering salvoes, would be relatively ineffective. The Navy did continue to develop a guided version of the 5in destroyer shell, which (by default) would be the only available future fire support weapon, but it, too, was afflicted by high costs. Such fiscal issues will presumably become more pressing as the Reagan Administration is forced to reduce defence spending over the next few years.

The continued existence of the four battleships was the only bright spot in this gloomy picture. As the war in Vietnam escalated, naval gunfire support became more and more valuable, and by 1966 the Department of Defense was considering recommissioning either one battleship or two heavy cruisers. Senator Richard B Russell was a strong advocate of the battleship. However, the then Chief of Naval Operations, Admiral David L MacDonald, strongly opposed it, and the decision to recommission *New Jersey* was not announced until the day after he left office, the following year. Modernisation was purposely made extremely austere, to avoid criticism that the ship was intended more as an admiral's flagship than for shore bombardment. Thus, although the ship had served as a flagship in the past, her admiral's quarters were deliberately not overhauled. It was claimed at the time that 80 per cent of all naval targets in Vietnam were within 16in gun range of the coast, and during her brief deployment *New Jersey* fired 5688 16in shells, compared to 771 during the whole of World War II.

Even so, critics of battleship reactivation remained active. In particular, as a Congressman, Melvin Laird had criticised the battleship decision. He became Secretary of Defense after Richard Nixon became President in January 1969. Some argued at the time that Secretary Laird personally ordered *New Jersey* decommissioned in 1969, as she was preparing for a second Vietnam deployment. The Navy Department went so far as to consider disposing of all four surviving battleships in 1973; the *New Jersey* and *Missouri* were to have been preserved as memorials. However, they were retained in view of their unique shore bombardment capability. They were, moreover, relatively youthful in terms of time spent in active service. *Missouri*, for example, was commissioned in 1944 and decommissioned in 1955, after only 11 years. Her sister ships were all laid up in the late 1940s, as part of a series of economy moves, and were recommissioned for Korea, then withdrawn in 1957-58. As of 1977, the Board of Inspection and Survey estimated that each had at least 15 remaining years.

MODERNISATION DECISION
It is difficult to trace the precise origins of the decision to modernise and recommission the battleships. As early as 1975, an analyst at the Center for Naval Analyses suggested that battleships might replace carriers in forward areas in time of crisis. They would be better able to survive an initial Soviet surprise attack, even though they would have nothing like the firepower of a carrier. They might, moreover, be able to engage Soviet ships at considerable distances, using guided shells. In 1969, in connection with the recommissioning of *New Jersey*, the Naval Ordnance Laboratory experimented with sub-calibre shells that could be fired from a 16in/50 gun. It appeared that a 280mm round could reach about 100,000 yards (50nm). At this time many thousands of such shells remained, non-nuclear relics of the Army 'atomic cannon' programme. In combat the ship fired only 16in rounds, but the potential to reach beyond twice conventional gun range remained and, indeed, remains now.

By about 1977 there was some Navy interest in recommissioning. The Board of Inspection and Survey examined all four ships and found them fundamentally sound. Early in 1980 one battleship, *New Jersey*, was tentatively included in the FY81 (Carter) budget, along with the proposal to refurbish the aircraft carrier *Oriskany*. Some regarded the battleship as a rival to the carrier project; others suggested that the battleship had been included as a kind of sacrificial lamb, in the expectation that one or the other, but not both, would be killed in committee. In fact both died, but the battleship came quite close to realisation. At this time it was estimated that an austere refit, incorporating NATO Sea Sparrow missiles for self-defence, would cost $225 million in FY80 dollars, or $270 million in FY81 funds; modernisation would take 12–15 months.

A retired USAF fighter pilot and Washington defence consultant, Charles E Myers, is credited with publicising the merits of a battleship under the designation 'interdiction assault ship'. He was particularly interested in the all-weather capability inherent in 16in guns. It is not clear at this remove whether Myers originated the idea or whether he was an early proponent, eg of an idea originated by the Marines, who certainly wanted the ship. Certainly the battleship was part of the official Navy budget request by February 1980. It did not survive the process of budget-cutting, but funds for *New Jersey* were included in the Reagan Administration's FY81 Supplemental budget.

New Jersey with a helicopter overhead just after she first fired into Lebanon. She can operate 3 helicopters.

UPI

NEW JERSEY CONVERSION

Out of a total cost of about $326 million, $170 million went for rehabilitation. The rest bought a variety of new systems: four octuple armoured box launchers for Tomahawk land-attack and long range anti-ship missiles; four quadruple launchers for Harpoon anti-ship missiles; four Phalanx close-in defensive guns; improved communications (to cruiser standard); SLQ-32 defensive ECM gear; and a new SPS-49 air search radar. The stern was cleared to provide one operating helicopter spot and three parking spots. Four twin 5in/38 guns were landed to make space for the Tomahawk launchers. The ship was converted to use Navy distillate fuel, rather than black oil, and her firefighting facilities were improved.

Once the project had been approved, it moved very rapidly. The design team was assembled aboard the ship at Long Beach, and given a very short time to complete work. Deadlines were also used to force the hands of the many offices within the Office of the Chief of Naval Operations. In other cases, each branch might have many chances ('chops') to review a given project, each 'chop' adding delay. In this case, everyone was allowed only a single 'chop'. As a result, *New Jersey* was converted on time and to cost, a salutary example for other shipbuilding projects.

The austerity of the conversion was justified, at the time, by the urgent need to reinforce US amphibious forces, and by the expectation that more might be accomplished in a future second and third phase. After all, a battleship is an enormous platform, and her sheer size invites proposals for installations such as the Aegis air defence system and a flight deck, aft. More recently the phase two plan has been abandoned, although the ships will receive better command and control systems. Thus it is most unlikely that the radical proposals for VSTOL flight decks and heavy batteries of vertically-launched missiles (either cruise or defensive) will ever materialise. The deterrent is the sheer cost of such radical alterations as the removal of No 3 turret.

New Jersey was funded under the FY81 and FY82 budgets, the latter providing long-lead funds for *Iowa*, which was fully funded under FY83 and should be recommissioned in April 1984, well ahead of the originally planned date of January 1985. Preliminary work began in October 1982. In theory, two battleships provide a minimum force sufficient to support simultaneous Marine operations in both oceans. However, at least one ship will always have to be refitting or working up, so three is a more realistic figure. The Navy failed to obtain funds for *Missouri* in FY84, but will try again in the current (FY85) budget. As this is written, it is not clear whether *Wisconsin* will be refitted.

New Jersey has now been in service for a little over a year, proving her versatility in each of the numbered fleets, and firing her 16in and 5in guns in anger for the first time in 14 years off Lebanon (14 December 1983 – 26 February 1984). There, the loss of US carrier attack aircraft proved Myers' point: no one can shoot down or capture a 16in shell. On the other hand the effectiveness of *New Jersey*'s shelling, and the spotting arrangements for it, is something of a mystery.

As a footnote, it may be worth noting that Congressional critics of the battleship programme suggested the two surviving *Des Moines* class cruisers as alternatives. Studies showed that they were deficient in the deck area required to fit cruise missile launchers: only a very large ship has sufficient area sufficiently isolated from the blast of heavy guns. The project manager of the design felt that the best alternative was, alas, long gone: he wished the two *Alaska*s had not been broken up in 1961, after so little active service. After all, in a world of unarmoured ships, even they would have been well-protected. As it is, then, the battleships seems to have been the best alternative. If the Navy has its way, they will remain in service through the rest of this century, and will see their 60th birthdays.

The Building of HMS Duke of York

by Ian Buxton

Duke of York was the third ship of the *King George V* class of battleship; 35,000 tons standard, ten 14in and 16 5.25in guns. Her hull and machinery were ordered from John Brown's Clydebank yard on 28 April 1937 as Contract No 554. She was laid down on 5 May 1937, launched 28 February 1940 and completed 4 November 1941. All photographs are from the author's collection courtesy of Upper Clyde Shipbuilders Ltd (Clydebank Division).

Duke of York's forward structure takes shape in July 1938. The protective bulkhead runs beneath the line of shadow cast on the deck plating, outboard of which is the cellular air/liquid/air anti-torpedo sandwich. Inboard are electrical breaker spaces and the ring main. The two nearest ladders lead down to what will become the damage control centre and low power rooms on the lower deck. Forward of the transverse bulkhead on frame 119 is 'B' turret space.

1

A view from aft also taken in July 1938. Plating being laid
amidships is covering the after machinery spaces at middle
deck level, ie two below the upper deck. 'Y' turret will be
installed between the two transverse bulkheads. The liner
Queen Elizabeth can be seen approaching the launching stage
on the next berth.

1 The starboard outer shaft bracket being lifted into place, ready
  for the palms to be rivitted to the supporting structure. Since
  the light cranes seen in the earlier photographs, could not lift
  such loads, sheers had to be rigged; the legs are clearly seen.

2 So that's how it was done. Tongued and grooved cemented
  side armour plates 15in thick and weighing some 40 tons were
  fitted after launch, and fixed with armour bolts through the
  shell plating tapped into the back of the plate. Photograph
  taken on 29 March 1940.

3 Curved armour 11-13in thick for 'B' twin 14in barbette
  surrounds in ring bulkhead. The planing mechanism for
  machining the roller path is being dismantled. The time is May
  1940 so that the ships behind the destroyer *Noble* (launched 7
  May) and the destroyer depot ship, *Hecla* (launched 14 March).

2

3

Superstructure erection in the region of the wardroom and planking of the upper deck are well under way (about August 1940). Casemates for the after twin 5.25in gun mounts are nearly complete. The compressed air main to operate the rivetting and caulking tools is visible. The destroyers behind are probably *Nerissa* and *Nizam*.

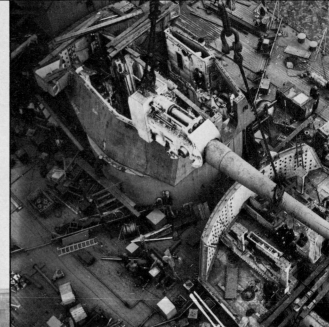

1 Machinery long since shipped and uptakes installed, the foward funnel is fitted in May 1941.

2 What it's all about. The 92-ton lefthand 14in gun for 'B' turret is lifted by Clydebank's 150-ton cantilever crane in July 1941. The trunnions and pins are clearly visible near the rear of the gun to permit elevation to 40°, but necessitating a 12-ton balance weight around the breech. Holes in the 7in rear of the turret are for ventilation.

3 Looking more like a battleship in June 1941, but directors, some 5.25in mounts and close range armament have yet to be fitted.

4 Forward superstructure with 8-barrelled pompoms and their controllers, 44in searchlights, 20in signal projectors, main director with Type 284 radar and two Mark V high-angle directors with Type 285. The 20mm Oerlikon gun pits are still empty.

5 Just what the modelmaker ordered. A midships view taken on 6 September 1941, two months before completion but with RN ratings already aboard.

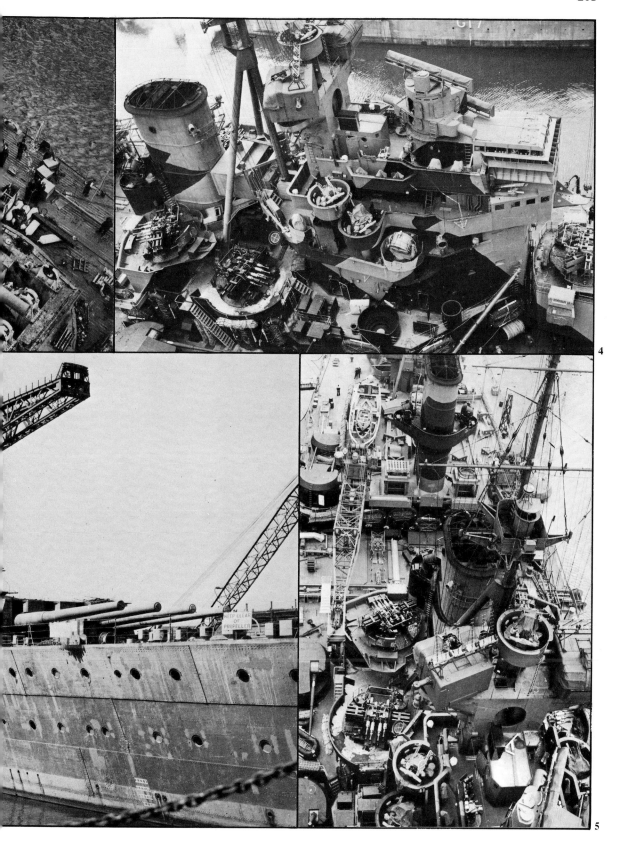

Almost ready to leave (6 September 1941)) boats shipped,
aircraft/boat cranes stowed, Carley floats and flotanets fitted.
The destroyer *Onslow* lies on the port side.

Duke of York leaves Clydebank on 7 September 1941,
assisted by the tug/tender *Paladin*, drawing 31ft amidships.

Arethusa Class Cruisers Part 1

By Alan Pearsall

Arethusa at sea August 1915. She never had a mast aft. Her only boats in this picture are the two sea boats forward. Commodore Tyrwhitt's broad pendant can just be seen at the truck, while at the port yardarm is the Red Ensign flown by British ships to avoid confusion with the Imperial German Ensign. She has the AA gun aft.
NMM

Trywhitt's *Arethusa* was perhaps the most famous cruiser of the 1914-18 War. Her seven sisters took a prominent part in the sea war. Yet the eight ships are relatively unfamiliar, even to students of warship design. They were all completed after the outbreak of war had imposed censorship, and, unlike their immediate successors, they all disappeared relatively quickly after the war. Technically as well as historically, however, they were an important and formative design, and richly deserve the fuller description now attempted, while the illustrations will, in addition, support their claims to be regarded as among the more handsome warships of the steam era.

To understand the background of their design is almost to review the development and purpose of the cruiser in the Royal Navy. From its inception in the 1880s the type had evolved into larger and smaller classes. Their purpose was, in fleet work, to scout ahead and around seeking information about the enemy and foiling the similar efforts of their opposite numbers. Cruisers were also employed in the protection of trade and possessions overseas. Usually operating independently. In both cases the larger cruisers acted as powerful supports to their smaller consorts. The qualities required were speed, radius of action and reasonable armament, but always with regard to size, because it will be clear that numbers of ships were often as useful as individual size and power. Thus we find attempts – not always successful – to design small and powerful cruisers which could be built in quantity.

In the late nineteenth and early twentieth centuries, the advent of torpedo craft introduced a new element. The early destroyers needed a larger warship in support, to provide quarters for the flotilla commander and his staff and to watch over the affairs of the sometimes frail torpedo craft. The high speed of the latter, however, complicated the naval architect's problem even more, and, in the Royal Navy, a third group of cruisers appeared to meet this need – the so-called 'scouts'. Between 1904 and 1912 large armoured cruisers, medium cruisers and these light fast 'scouts' were all built, often contemporaneously.

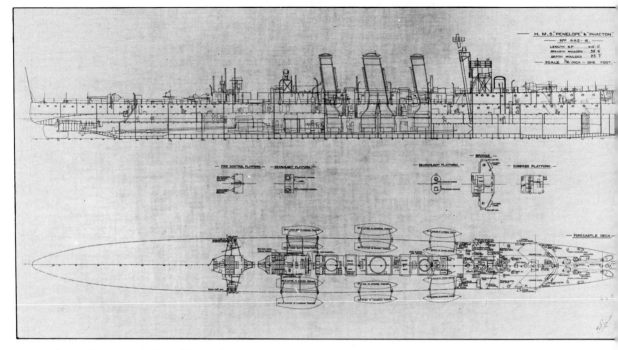

¹⁄₁₆in = 1ft elevation and deck plans of the *Arethusa* class cruisers *Penelope* and *Phaethon* as completed1914–15.
NMM

By contrast, the German Navy built only a few armoured cruisers and otherwise followed a steady line of development of light cruisers, each group being slightly larger and faster than its predecessor. Both navies agreed, however, that, for light cruisers, the 4in gun was most suitable, and this was the armament of the British 'P' class of 1898, the 'Gems' of 1903-4, and the various scouts from 1904 onwards.

By 1912, the development of the destroyer had produced a situation where the existing flotilla cruisers of the 'scout' and *Boadicea* types were becoming barely adequate, and service opinion of them was unfavourable. Their speed of about 25 knots was now becoming too slow for accompanying destroyers that could maintain nearly 30 knots at sea, while their armament of 4in guns now gave support only by numbers rather than calibre. German destroyers certainly retained the 3.4in gun rather longer than did British, but, on the other hand, they tended to be rather faster than British equivalents. A case therefore existed for further development of the 'destroyer cruiser'.

Meanwhile another line of development had run its course. The Town' class had been built first under the 1908 Programme as a more powerful fast cruiser and successive versions had followed, until it was felt that the type had become rather large although in other respects excellent ships. In some of them, an armoured belt instead of a protective deck, was introduced for the first time in small cruisers.

The advent to the Admiralty of Winson Churchill brought not only that inquiring and forceful mind to bear on these problems, but also that of the equally forceful Lord Fisher, upon whom Churchill relied for much technical advice. The combination, in fact, added another reason for an improved cruiser design, when they decided that the battleship of the 1912 Programme should be a fast division capable of 25 knots, thus emphasising the Fleet's weakness, which the appearance of the battlecruisers had already indicated, in having no cruisers of any greater speed. This contradiction, however, produced a disagreement on the cruisers of 1912 between Churchill and Fisher.

DESIGN HISTORY

Churchill had the Director of Naval Construction produce a design based on the *Active*, the latest 'scout'. The original proposals were for a 'Super-*Active*' of 3500 tons, oil-fired for 30 knots, armed either with ten 4in guns, or two 6in and four 12pdrs, the latter subsequently being modified to two 6in and four 4in. However, another proposal was made, for a 'Super-*Swift*' with six 4in and 40 knots, and this was strongly supported by Fisher, if it did not actually emanate from him. Fisher disliked small cruisers anyway, holding the view that they lost their speed quickly in a seaway, and, worse still, that they would be 'all gobbled up by an armoured cruiser, like the armadillo gobbles up the ants – puts out its tongue and licks them up one after another – and the bigger the ant, the more placid the digestive smile'. The 'Super-*Swift*' could escape, however, and draw the enemy on to another of Fisher's great visions, the Big Submarine.

Churchill, supported by Jellicoe, held out for the 'Super-*Actives*', pointing out that they were fast and

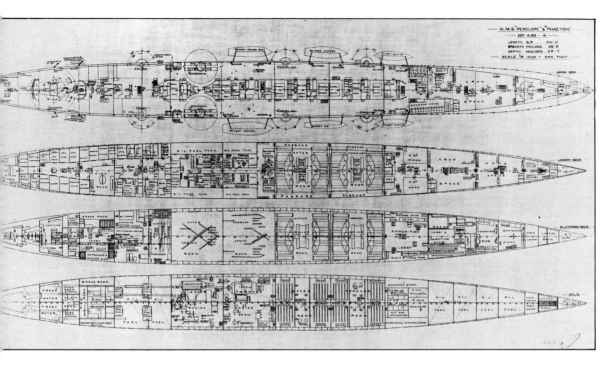

powerful enough to be 'destroyers of destroyers', and that it was intended to continue in these ships the fitting of armoured belts as in the later 'Town' class. From these views, they could not be shaken.

The question of numbers also arose acutely. For some years past, the estimates had provided only for four or five light cruisers each year, a number which was barely sufficient to keep pace with German construction without allowing either for the much wider British responsibilities or for the inferior position of the defender against an attacker with the choice of place and time of attack. Even in 1912, Churchill proposed 'chucking two *Dartmouths* and a *Blonde* and scraping round to get four "Super-*Actives*" instead'. But a paper by Troubridge pointed out the inferiority of the British position and the programme was increased to eight ships both in 1912 and 1913. These 16 additional light cruisers were, as it turned out, just in time.

The design was, of course, prepared in the office of the Director of Naval Construction, then Sir Philip Watts, by the cruiser section under W H Whiting, S V Goodall, later to be DNC himself, doing the detailed work, which took place in the first half of 1912. The result was conventional in outline, based very much on the *Active*, but rather larger, faster, oil-fired and armoured. The new features were thus to be incorporated in a tried framework, in the best form of technical development. The hull form was tested at Haslar, after which the beam was reduced by a foot, though the full results were not available until the contracts had been let, and the *Caroline*s embodied the test results to the full. The hull was very fine, with a square section and bilge keels. The original stipulation that the side must be straight where it was armoured was waived, as the design developed, again to the improvement of the hull

form. This condition was intended to avoid complicated arrangements where the belt ended and a protective deck began fore and aft, but it was decided instead to continue the belt right up to the stem and further aft at 2in thickness. The main belt was 3in High Tensile (HT) steel, and the plates, some very large, were all worked so that they formed part of the strength of the ship, thus saving a good deal of weight. A 1in deck was fitted aft over the steering engine compartment. The upper deck amidships was also in 1in HT steel, although this was as much for strength as protection, as the impossibility of carrying the lower deck through the boiler rooms required deep web frames, extra cross beams and other measures to ensure the strength of the hull, a problem accentuated by the intention to carry fuel in the ends and thus creating a high hogging bending movement. In an attempt to ensure dryness forward, increased flare was given to the forcastle.

MACHINERY
The machinery of the new cruisers also broke new ground. The enterprise of the Italians in their light cruiser *Quarto* was, it was thought, being followed by the Germans in using fast-running destroyer-type turbines in larger ships, and the *Arethusa*s consequently became the first British major warships to be so equipped. The power required to reach the desired speed of 30 knots was high even by battleship standards. Although geared turbines were considered, they were not felt to have proved themselves and four screws were to be fitted, each driven by a 7500shp direct drive turbine running at 590rpm which could give 1000shp at 650rpm for some hours when required. The outer shafts were driven from the forward engine room, the inner from the after. Forward of the engine room were

Undaunted in the Clyde 1914, second ship of the class. She alone had no searchlight platform on the mast and her 4in guns still have no shields.

NMM

two boiler rooms, each with four Yarrow water-tube boilers working at 235lb per sq in. When tenders for the machiner were called for, a curious episode occurred, as all the tenderers quoted to the Admiralty specification, but also submitted alternatives, professedly more economical. As a result, all the six vessels with Parsons turbines also had cruising turbines fitted geared to the outer shafts, to run at a more economical speed. The other two ships had Brown-Curtis turbines, but no cruising turbines.

ARMAMENT

There was much discussion over the armament. The first draft suggested two 6in and four 12pdrs, but this seems quickly to have been replaced by a wholly 4in armament, either ten, as in the *Active* or 12, but in either case to be a new mark of quickfiring gun instead of the ordinary breechloading (BL) guns hitherto used. These guns were to be mounted, again as before, along both sides. Twelve guns, it was found, meant too many men to be carried, and ten became the armament finally approved, with men to fight seven, ie both forecastle and quarter-deck guns (two each) and one side of three. Two single torpedo-tubes were also to be carried. However, there were those who remained unhappy about 4in guns only and it would be interesting to speculate on the success of the *Arethusa*s if they had been completed with their original armament.

Despite the great shortage of light cruisers in 1914-15, the immediately preceding *Active*s and *Blonde*s, upon which the design was based, took a very

minor part in the war, hardly comparable, say, to the early 'Town' class. Late in 1912, however, following the appointment of Rear-Admiral Sir Archibald Moore and Controller, it was again proposed to fit a 6in gun fore and aft, each replacing two 4in. Only minor alterations were necessary, principally raising the conning tower, bridge and funnels 3½ft. The bigger guns meant a slight increase in weight, but the advantage of making the ships rather more than large destroyers was well worth this handicap. Although this proposal was approved by by Bridgeman, then First Sea Lord, and by Churchill, the argument was reopened when the armament of the 1913 cruisers came to be discussed, as there was the question of using the redundant 4in on these ships.

Even at this stage, the all 4in armament was still in the field, although, already, advanced thinkers had gone to an all 6in armament too. In favour of the 4in it was asserted that they could cope with any German destroyer (and indeed light cruisers), that the cruiser would not be tempted to engage superior enemies, that a mixed armament was unsatisfactory in a small ship, and that 6in shell was too heavy to be handled in such small and lively vessels. The advocates of the 6in, however, believed in fitting the largest gun reasonably possible and thus producing more powerful ships, with a marked superiority over destroyers, while a single-calibre armament needed fewer men yet gave greater fighting power. In the end, a curious compromise was reached, after a conference of cruiser admirals. The 1913 cruisers, the *Caroline*s, were to have two 6in aft to allow the ship to protect herself from a chasing cruiser, while eight 4in forward and on the sides would deal with destroyers from wherever they might come. It was suggested that the *Arethusa*s should also be fitted with this extremely odd, for a British ship at least, arrangement of guns. The DNC, however, strongly opposed this suggestion, as the extra weight involved in extending the superstructure was serious in itself, and would also adversely affect the trim. The original modification was therefore allowed to remain. The weight problem was one which became increasingly serious both for the *Arethusa*s and their successors.

The torpedo armament also caused some trouble. It was feared that the 21in torpedo proposed would not stand being fired from the upper deck. The original intention was therefore to fit submerged tubes, but no room could be found for them. A lower deck mounting was suggested, but, again, space could not be found for a training tube, while the deck height was insufficient for loading. An upper deck mounting had therefore to be accepted, at first only with single tubes, but twin tubes were soon fitted to make up the salvo of two which seems to have been considered all that was needed at this time – as in contemporary destroyers and the 'E' class submarines. The final armament was two 6in Mark XII on PIX mountings, six 4in Mark V, one 3in AA and four 21in torpedo tubes. Fire control arrangements were of the rudimentary pre-director

Phaeton goes on her 1914 trials in the Clyde looking throughly disarranged. The two ensigns may be noted. She has sponsons under each 4in gun, and poles up on the radio aerials, as well is the full complement of boats.
P A Vicary

type, there being a control position on the bridge and another at the after end of the superstructure, with voice pipe and 'navyphones' to guns and tubes. Each control position had a rangefinder and two searchlights. An armoured conning tower was, as was then customary, provided on the forecastle, with an armoured tube to the transmitting station below. There were magazines and shell rooms fore and aft, with a long supply route to the broadside guns.

The design as a whole was a very finely balanced one. It will be clear from the foregoing that there was no space to spare, and the weights were equally closely drawn. Although there was a Board margin of 20 tons when the design was approved by the Board in July 1912, it quickly disappeared under the usual small additions and alterations, and, indeed, the *Caroline*s once again started the tendency to enlarge, by being 10ft longer.

Invitations to tender were sent out in July 1912 and orders were placed in September. One ship was allotted to Chatham Yard and another to Devonport, while the remainder were to be built by contract by Fairfields (one), Vickers (two) and Beardmores (three). Each of these firms was to engine its ships, but for dockyard-built ships, an attempt was made to help the Thames Ironworks Co, then in the hands of a receiver, in the hope that they could, with such a contract, surmount their difficulties. But the hope was vain, and eventually the Chatham ship was engined by Fairfields and the Devonport one by the Parsons Company.

Three views of the *Arethusa* when new shows the handsome appearance of the class to good advantage. She has not been fitted with the centre pair of davits and the whaler lies at the boom. She has canvas screens along the waist. The rigging of the radio aerials shows well in the quarter view.

NMM

TURBINES AND BOILERS

Six of the ships had Parsons impulse-reaction turbines, with cruising turbines fitted on the outside shafts. *Arethusa* and *Undaunted* engined by Fairfields were fitted with Brown-Curtis short type turbines without cruising turbines. Designed shp was 30,000shp at 590rpm for 28 knots, with an eight hour overload to 650rpm for 40,000shp and 30 knots. Although these turbines ran at a much higher speed than previous designs, and the builders all expressed misgivings about the low weights specified by the Admiralty, no serious trouble was experienced in the upshot, and similar machinery was fitted in subsequent light cruisers. The cruising turbines, however, do not appear to have been much used, as they took 20-25 minutes to connect up.

Eight Yarrow water-tube boilers were provided working at 235lb per sq in and with a heating surface of 42,400 sq ft, and with forced draught. Succeeding light cruisers again had similar installations.

OIL FUEL

The use of oil fuel was one of the *Arethusa*s great advantages over their predecessors, both in giving higher speed and in avoiding the delay and exhaustion of coaling. But several difficulties were found. The original scheme was to use all the double bottom for fuel, as well as four tanks forward of the fore magazine, two between after engine room and after magazine and two (known as 'peace tanks') over the engine rooms above water. It was first of all felt that the fuel under the boilers might heat dangerously when the boilers were fully extended. Then it was found that some of the oil was so viscous that heating had to be fitted in the tanks. Finally the peace tanks were seen to be a possible danger, as even if the fuel was used first, the vapour left could be dangerous in action. They could also have an adverse effect on stability. In practice, they were filled with 50 tons or so instead of their full capacity of 150 tons, the fuel was used first, and then the tanks were filled with water. Such tanks were not repeated, and their omission contributed to the improved accommodation of subsequent classes. The total oil stowage was 810 tons.

1

FUEL CONSUMPTION

The fuel consumption of all the *Arethusa*s and their direct-drive successors seems to have been similar, using about 550 tons a day at 29 knots and 260 tons at 24, with 96 at 16 on main engines, and only 60 on the cruising turbines at that speed. The subsequent geared-turbine cruisers saved about 100 tons a day at the higher speeds.

Expressed in the customary manner, the radius of action of the class was:

100 miles at 29 knots (1½ days)
1700 miles at 24 knots (3 days)
3200 miles at 16 knots (8 days)
5000 miles at 16 knots (13 days) cruising turbines.

Names were given to the ships from traditional frigate sources and none, indeed, had been out of the Navy List very long. The Chatham ship, laid down in No 7 Dry Dock on 28 October 1912, became *Arethusa* and gave her name to the class. The *Aurora* at Devonport was actually begun four days earlier, while the contract ships, *Undaunted* at Fairfields, *Phaeton* and *Penelope* at Barrow and *Galatea, Inconstant* and *Royalist* were all laid down by June 1913. The first launch was in September 1913, and when war broke out on 4 August 1914, three of the ships were very near completion – the *Arethusa* was actually commissioned at Chatham on 11 August by Captain B S Thesiger, *Aurora* and *Undaunted* followed within the next month.

The trials of the *Arethusa* were highly unsatisfactory, not only because she did not apparently make her speed, but also because they were run in shallow water in the Thames Estuary, with unreliable bearings as marks; some defects also developed. The DNC therefore demanded that the next ships should be properly tried as much depended on them, with the *Caroline*s coming on fast, and further developments of the type in prospect. Furthermore, it was never expected that the

2

*Arethusa*s would make their full speed without some trials of propellers to achieve the best design. And, of course, there was the extra weight, such as 37 tons more in the machinery, 29 tons in the 6in guns and five for twin tubes. Both *Aurora* and *Undaunted* were therefore tried on the Polperro (Cornwall) and Skelmorlie measured miles respectively, where they reached 28½ to 29 knots with the full 40,000shp.

No extensive trials of propellers were undertaken, so that this was the most usual performance of the class. When they went into service, they were found to be very wet forward, but were good sea boats, and never seem to have abandoned an operation on account of bad weather. One complaint was indeed recorded in 1915, but the DNC held this to be only what might be

1 *Galatea* at anchor with short topgallant mast. She could be distinguished by the wings to the upper bridge. The motor boat in the after davits shows well.
IWM

2 *Inconstant* in her early days, also with short topgallant mast.
IWM

expected from a small ship in the North Sea. The *Arethusa*s trimmed by the bow, which may partly explain their wetness, and the 10ft longer *Caroline*s were apparently much drier. All the later 'Cs', however, were liable to take water badly over the forecastle, and trawler bows were eventually fitted to the last ones. *To be continued*

BOOK REVIEWS

DÖNITZ – THE LAST FÜHRER
Portrait of a Nazi War Leader by Peter Padfield.
Published by Victor Gollancz February 1984.
525pp (23.5cm × 17.5cm) 32 photographs, 2 maps,
index ISBN 0 575 03186 7 (£12.95).

Mr Padfield has written a long account of the life and career of the late Grand Admiral Karl Dönitz (1892-1980). In it he argues that Dönitz became a fanatical Nazi whose U-Boat Arm was a tool for German world domination. Further he alleges that Dönitz gave tacit, if not active approval to the genocide programme. He also states that the U-boat threat was a mere chimera, never posing a serious threat to Great Britain and her will to continue to fight.

The military argument appears sporadically throughout the work, with a concentration (strangely) in the last pages on Dönitz's appreciation of the naval situation and U-boat strength and capabilities on the eve of the Second World War. Could the U-Boat Arm have brought Great Britain to her knees if all available submarines had been concentrated in the Atlantic at the start of hostilities – assuming that Dönitz had had the 300 U-boats he stated were necessary for the task? Mr Padfield says no.

In the initial period of the U-boat war, up to the middle of 1940, the sinking figures were low, but they began to rise dramatically, especially when the French west coast bases had been secured. By the end of 1941 they had once more begun to fall. On 11 December 1941, in the euphoria of the immediate aftermath of Pearl Harbor, Hitler declared war on the United States and Dönitz ordered the start of Operation *Paukenschlag* ('Drumbeat') and sinkings rose to unprecedented heights.

This was in fact one of Dönitz's most serious mistakes, and was compounded by the decision to undertake 'tonnage war' rather than the far more worrying form – economic warfare directly mounted against shipping around the one American springboard into Europe – the British Isles. The author does refer to the two forms of warfare, but fails to explore them; there is little doubt that fear of the effects of concerted U-boat warfare was very much in Churchill's mind at the time. From the evidence in the Public Record Office and elsewhere the disruption of the eastbound Atlantic convoys could have caused the withdrawal of British participation in the Second World War.

The results off the East Coast of the United States were undoubtedly encouraging, but when forced by the institution of convoy there to return to the North Atlantic convoy routes, the Allies were still unsure of their ability to deal with the menace until the resounding successes of spring 1943. Mr Padfield seems to be unaware of the main axiom of the Principles of War, which states that once the aim is selected it must be maintained.

The author also puts too much significance on the figure of 300 U-boats that Dönitz considered necessary to close the Atlantic to shipping bound for England. His appreciation (see above) was an example of frustration if not consternation at war being declared by Great Britain long before Hitler had said the massive Z-Plan Fleet need be ready (between 1946 and 1948). Both Grand Admiral Raeder and Dönitz were in agreement that the only resort lay in U-boats because they took less time to build. Therein lies Dönitz's reasoning – at least eventually there would be something for the Navy to do in the war; as it was they could merely demonstrate that men of the *Kriegsmarine* would show others how to die well.

The further argument that had there been 300 boats, then all resources of the Royal Navy would be concentrated on one single route, is an over-simplification, as well as a recipe for disaster. Incidentally, the comment that aircraft carriers would be included in escorts is countered by two factors: First, there was no efficient anti-submarine bomb in service at the time, and second, the *Courageous* sinking. Only three years later did the escort carrier begin to take a toll of U-boats, and by then the enemy had been forced away from the main northern convoy routes, submarine detection and attack techniques having undergone a revolution.

Mr Padfield argues in addition that had the Royal and Allied Navies been in any danger of losing the convoy war, the United States would have entered the war to combat the German threat. Here his knowledge of American history and politics is sadly lacking.

The real heart of the book lies however not in a detailed examination of the naval aspects of the Grand Admiral's life, but in the relationships between him and the Nazis. The early descriptions of his life are recounted to show a strict Prussian upbringing, yet demonstating that Dönitz as a young man was fascinated by the more esoteric things in life. There is also significant reference to the question of whether Dönitz was actually mentally unstable. This last point is both extraneous (surely a succession of Commanding Officers would have noticed), and as hurtful to his remaining family as are the allegations of rabid Nazism that follow.

The more serious allegation against Dönitz was, and is, that the September 1942 *Laconia* Order was a *carte-blanche* for U-boat commanders to shoot merchant ship survivors in the water. It seems strange that there was only one such incident during the war, and the very order caused problems of wording before it was transmitted. There is no doubt that at least some of the evidence adduced at the International Military Tribunal at Nüremberg was of dubious origin, especially as it came from deserters from the German Armed Forces. The claim that the Nazism allegation is further supported by the rhetorical nature of some of Dönitz's exhortatory speeches and his *assumed* presence at a genocide briefing by Himmler requires a lot of faith in any historian of the period – especially in view of the *débâcle* over the Hitler Diaries.

There is no doubt that Dönitz was not an entirely simple character, but Mr Padfield fails to publish the evidence so vehemently promised when talking to Mr Ludovic Kennedy ('Timewatch', February, BBC 2). It is not enough to throw mud; an historian must make it stick. Equally, no responsible historian should shrink from the unpalatable truth, even if it does cause a change in opinion; regrettably Mr Padfield has failed to alter this reviewer's opinion, but he had caused a number of further questions to be asked.

The books reads racily, with a journalistic flow, and can thus be assimilated readily, but the melange of fact, surmise and suspicion makes it a book for the specialist professional historian rather than the general reader.

David Westwood

OTHER BOOKS RECEIVED

The Great War at Sea 1914-1918 by Richard Hough (OUP, October 1983) 353pp, 41 photographs, 11 maps, index, £14.50, ISBN 0 19 215871 6, 9½in × 6in. A strange offering from OUP since it is no more than a popular, compressed version of Arthur Marder's famous five volumes on the *Dreadnought to Scapa Flow*. The post-Jutland period, more than half of hostilities, receives a handful of pages. The Grand Fleet and High Seas Fleet dominate to the exclusion of all else, especially the activities of the other major navies.

US Naval Developments by Jan S Breemer (Frederick Warne, February 1984) 194pp, photographs, 59 figures, tables and organisation charts, index, £14.95, ISBN 0 7232 3234 2, 9¾in × 6¾in. A compact fact-filled guide to the US Navy of the 1980s with a foreward by Norman Polmar. Four appendices detail its ships, aircraft, weapons and sensors. Chapter 5 refreshingly covers recruitment and manning problems.

The US Merchant Marine: in search of an enduring maritime policy by Clinton H Whitehurst, Jr (Naval Institute Press/Arms and Armour Press, March 1984) 330pp, 25 photographs, 39 tables and bibliography, glossary, index, £20.95, ISBN 0 87021 737 2, 9in × 5¾in. The first general survey of American shipping to be published since 1954. Clinton H Whitehurst and other specialist contributors from the industry provide 20 essays that cover history, government involvement, technology, the American seaman, ports, US-owned foreign flag shipping, inland movement of goods and rival fleets (especially the Soviet Union). Since 1954 the US merchant fleet has shrunk from 1123 ships to 500 (late 1982) and its world ranking from first place to eleventh. This is a comprehensive and strategic study taking in the Rapid Deployment Force and the naval role of merchant ships.

Sea Power in the Falklands by Captain Charles W Koburger, Jr, US Coast Guard Reserve (Retd) (Praeger, March 1984) 188pp, 19 photographs, 12 maps, index, £14.95, ISBN 0 03 069534 1, 9½in × 5¾in. A vigorously written analysis of the Falklands War from an American observer that has two particularly interesting chapters on Operation Rosario (the original Argentine invasion) and the *Armada Republica Argentina*. This short account has no revelations or axes to grind and is all the better for that.

A's & A's

CHINESE BATTLESHIPS *(Warship 29)* From Peter H Kuntz, Durmersheim, Germany
In the above cited article, the author states, that these two ships were the biggest warships completed for a foreign navy in Germany before World War I.

This is not quite true: In June 1900 AG Vulkan of Stettin completed the armoured cruiser *Yakumo* for the Japanese Navy. She was far bigger than the Chinese ships, having 10,288 tons in loaded condition. This ship served in the Japanese Navy for 46 years!

HMS QUEEN ELIZABETH *(Warship 29, photograph p 31)* From N J M Campbell, Ryde, Isle of Wight and J Dixon of Altrincham, Cheshire.
Aircraft were supplied to battleships of the Grand Fleet during the second half of 1918. Late October figures give the 5 *Queen Elizabeth*s as carrying a total of 3-1½ Strutters and 7 single-seaters, probably Camels as the Pup was being phased out, with platforms on B and X turrets. These platforms were not all identical, and some did not have the rails over the gun barrels which were needed for the 1½ Strutter.

Decapping armour was not fitted and the light line of B turret is believed to be due to sunlight falling on the edge of the 13in face plate where it joined the 11in armour of the rest of the turret.

The 3 patches visible on the photographs (on the shelter-deck screen above No 3 6in gun near the scuttles just above the open skylight and on the screen above as J Dixon has helpfully pointed out) were from hits by Turkish field guns on 5 March 1915. The damage report gives 18 hits by 2.8in percussion fuzed shrapnel from mobile guns. Next day there were 3 hits by 11in from the old battleship *Hairredin Barbarossa*, all on the side armour below water and causing very little damage. On 18 March there were 5 hits from 5.9in howitzers firing HE shell.

After Jutland *Warspite* had similar patches on her port quarter near the blanked off casemates. These scars remained with both ships until their reconstruction in the late 1930s.

COASTAL FORCES MISCELLANY From G M Hudson, Halifax, W Yorks.
In *Conway's All the World's Fighting Ships 1922-46*, reference will be found on page 67 to the first MTBs built for the Royal Navy since the First World War; the

60ft British Power Boat *MTB 1-12, 14-19*. Among the details of these 18 boats appears a note that, *MTB 1* was ex-*MTB 7*, *MTB 7* was ex-*MTB 13* and *MTB 19* was ex-*MTB 1*. A comment on these renumberings may be of interest.

The original *MTB 1*, was involved in extensive 'first of class' trials, from early 1936 until 1939. During this period she was under the charge of British Power Boats (BPB). She was commissioned temporarily on 23 June 1936, under Lieutenant-Commander G B Sayer RN and on 30 June, with *MTB 2*, also temporarily commissioned for the occasion, took part in a special demonstration for King Edward VIII. With the King, accompanied by the First Sea Lord and Commander Lord Louis Mountbatten, on board, *MTB 1* carried out a high speed attack, during which a practice torpedo was fired at the destroyer HMS *Amazon*. *MTB 1* was the first of His Majesty's Ships, in which King Edward VIII embarked after his accession and, after this exercise, she paid off and returned to BPB control.

By the end of 1936, the remaining boats of the 1935 Programme, *MTB 2-6*, had been accepted into service and it was decided to send a flotilla of this type to the Mediterranean, based on Malta. In order to bring the 1st MTB Flotilla up to full strength – six boats – and also present a logical numerical sequence, *MTB 7*, the first boat of the 1936 Programme, was renumbered *MTB 1 (ii)* in April 1937, becoming the Senior Officer's boat (Lt-Cdr G B Sayer RN). *MTB 1 (i)* then became *MTB 7 (ii)*.

A similar situation occurred in 1938. As *MTB 7 (ii)* ex-*MTB 1 (i)* was still running trials under BPB control, *MTB 13*, a 1937 Programme boat, which was still under construction at Hythe, was redesignated *MTB 7 (iii)* whereupon *MTB 7 (ii)* ex-*MTB 1 (i)* became *MTB 13 (ii)*. This enabled the 2nd MTB Flotilla, shipped in freighters to Hong Kong in September 1938, to comprise *MTB 7-12*.

The final MTB renumbering of the original boat took place in June 1938 when *MTB 13 (ii)*, ex-*MTB 7 (ii)*, ex-*MTB 1 (i)* became *MTB 19*, presumably as a result of the number '13' being considered unlucky. (This is borne out by an explanation of pendant numbers prior to 1948, where no pendant number '13' appears to have been in use, with one exception. For some reason *S 13* did get used; surprisingly there was a *MA/SB* (later *MGB 13*!).

It was however the following year before *MTB 19* was finally accepted by the Royal Navy, joining *MTB 14-18*, to form the 3rd MTB Flotilla. Originally intended for Singapore, these six boats actually joined the 1st Flotilla at Malta for the outbreak of World War II, before returning, via French rivers and canals, to Portsmouth on 8 December 1939.

The renumbering of the original *MTB 1* was by no means over when she finally entered service as *MTB 19*. Whilst the five most modern boats of the 1st MTB Flotilla, *MTB 14-18*, were ready to operate from their new base at Felixstowe by early 1940, the six older boats, *MTB 1-5* and *19*, were no longer considered fit for front line operations. (*MTB 6* had been lost through heavy weather off Sardinia on the return journey from

Malta to Portsmouth.) Consequently, in the late summer of 1940, these six boats were reclassified as Motor Attendant Craft and were renumbered *MAC 1-6* respectively.

It is understood that MAC were used as dispatch boats by Captains (Minesweepers), at Sheerness, Dover, Portsmouth, Harwich, and Grimsby, for visiting their flotilla at sea. These were requisitioned trawlers, presumably at that time in the war, not fitted with short-range radios.

The final reclassification and renumbering of these craft occurred in 1942. After service as MAC, several of these boats served on air/sea rescue duties during 1941/42, before being converted for target service duties in 1942. In her ultimate role, the original boat was again renumbered, becoming *C/T 06* and, as such, she appeared on the 'sale lists' issued postwar by the Director of Small Craft Disposals.